Great Songwriters

23 classic songs for keyboard

First published in 1994 by International Music Publications Ltd
International Music Publications Ltd is a Faber Music company
Bloomsbury House 74–77 Great Russell Street London WC1B 3DA
Music arranged & processed by Barnes Music Engraving Ltd
Printed in England by Caligraving Ltd

ISBN10: 0-571-53471-6
EAN13: 978-0-571-53471-5

BEWITCHED

Words by Lorenz Hart
Music by Richard Rodgers

Suggested Registration: Flute
Rhythm: Soft Rock
Tempo: ♩ = 80

Am
of it? He is cold, I a - gree.
F#A E♭
Dm7 G7 Dm7 G7 Em E♭dim
He can laugh, but I love it, al-though the laugh's on
Dm7 G7 C Dm7
me. I'll sing to him each Spring to him, and
Em E7 F Fm C D7
long for the day when I'll cling to him. Be - witched, bo-thered and be -
G7 C Fm C
- wild - ered am I.
A7 Am C C7 D7
Dm7 E♭dim E7 Em F
Fm G7

But Not For Me

Music and Lyrics by George Gershwin and Ira Gershwin

Suggested Registration: Vibraphone
Rhythm: Swing
Tempo: ♩ = 130

G7 C Am G7 C
I was a fool to fall and get that way.
G7 D7 G7 C
Heigh - ho! A - las! and al - so lack - a - day!
C7 F Dm7 C
Al - though I can't dis - miss the mem - 'ry of his kiss,
Am Dm7 G7 C F C
I guess he's not for me.

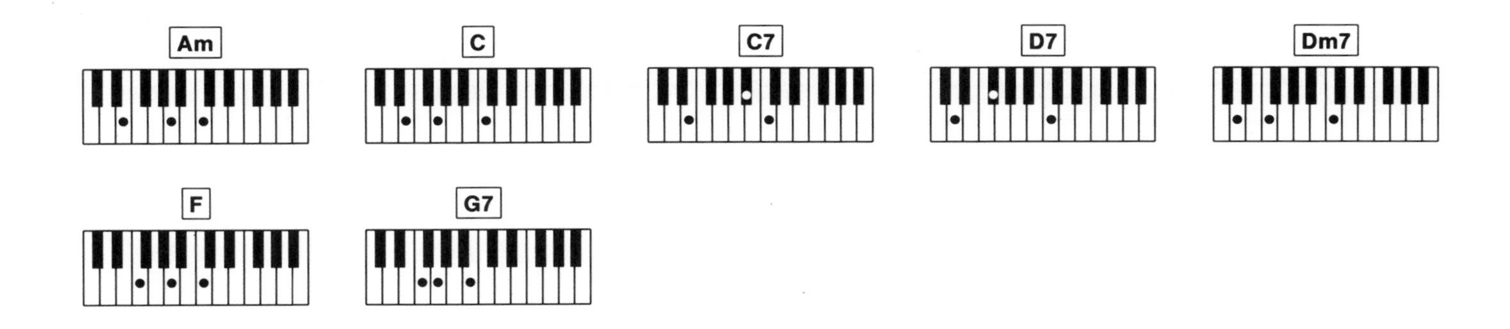
Am
C
C7
D7
Dm7
F
G7

Come Fly With Me

Words by Sammy Cahn / Music by James Van Heusen

Suggested Registration: Vibraphone
Rhythm: Swing
Tempo: ♩ = 128

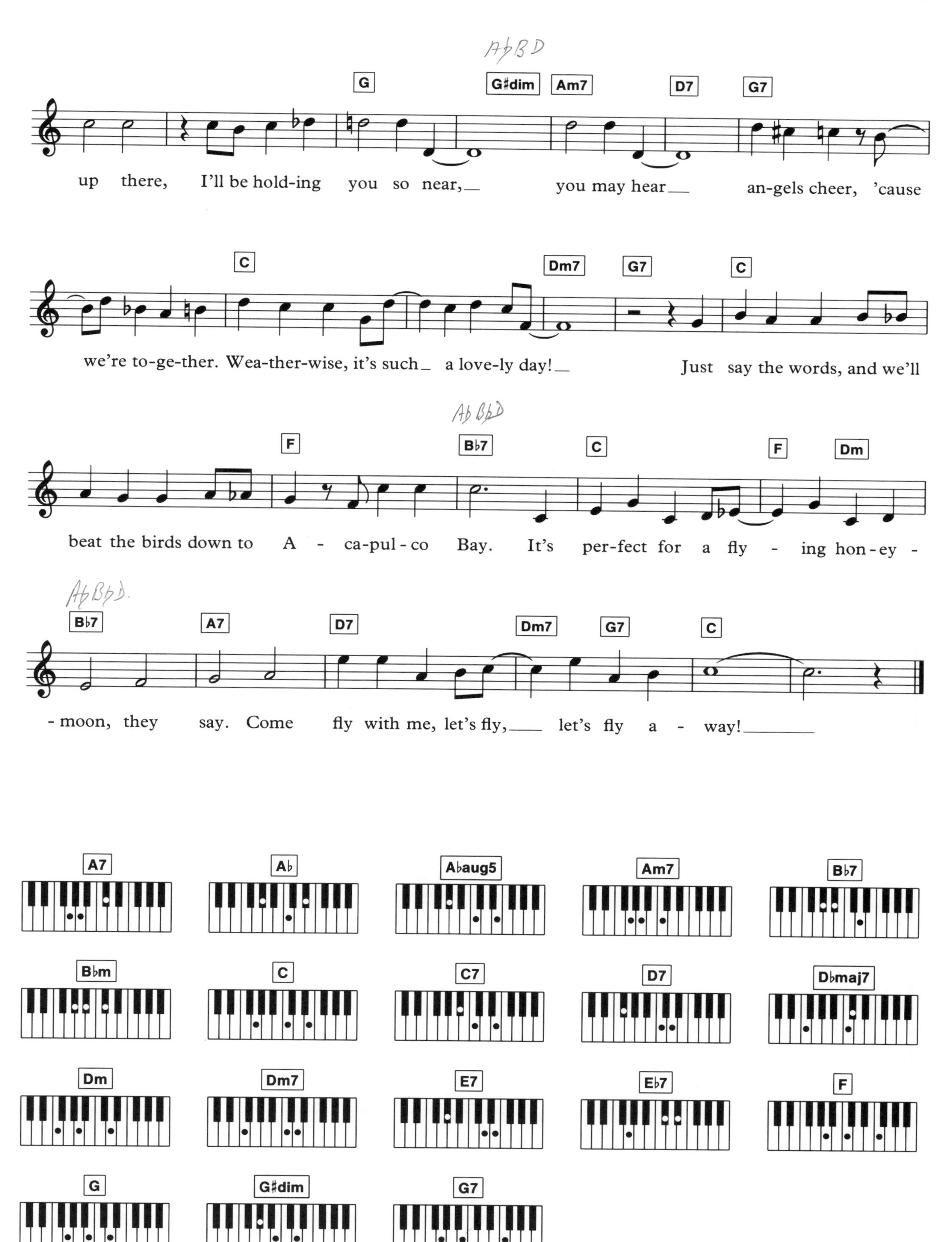
G G♯dim Am7 D7 G7
up there, I'll be hold-ing you so near, you may hear an-gels cheer, 'cause
C Dm7 G7 C
we're to-ge-ther. Wea-ther-wise, it's such a love-ly day! Just say the words, and we'll
F B♭7 C F Dm
beat the birds down to A - ca-pul-co Bay. It's per-fect for a fly - ing hon-ey -
B♭7 A7 D7 Dm7 G7 C
- moon, they say. Come fly with me, let's fly, let's fly a - way!
A7
A♭
A♭aug5
Am7
B♭7
B♭m
C
C7
D7
D♭maj7
Dm
Dm7
E7
E♭7
F
G
G♯dim
G7

EDELWEISS

Words by Oscar Hammerstein II
Music by Richard Rodgers

Suggested Registration: Accordian
Rhythm: Waltz
Tempo: ♩ = 108

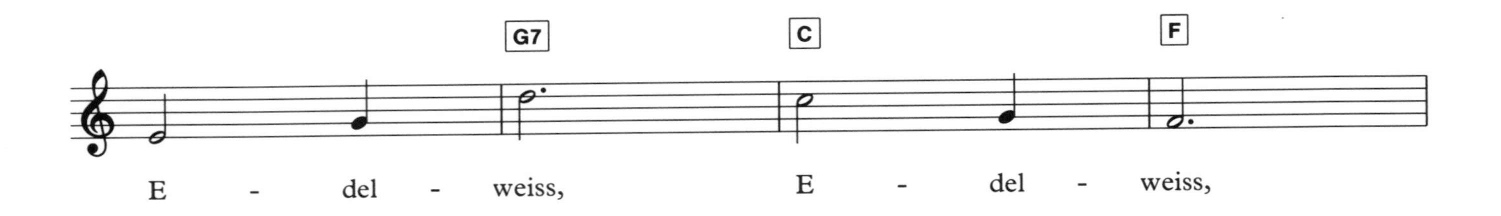

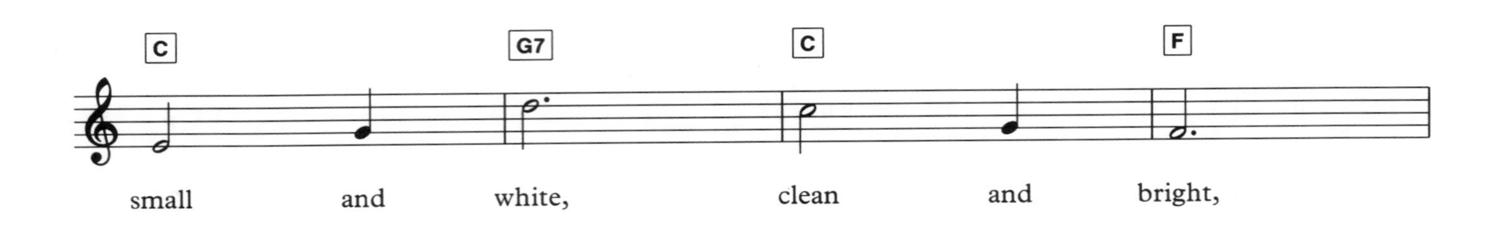

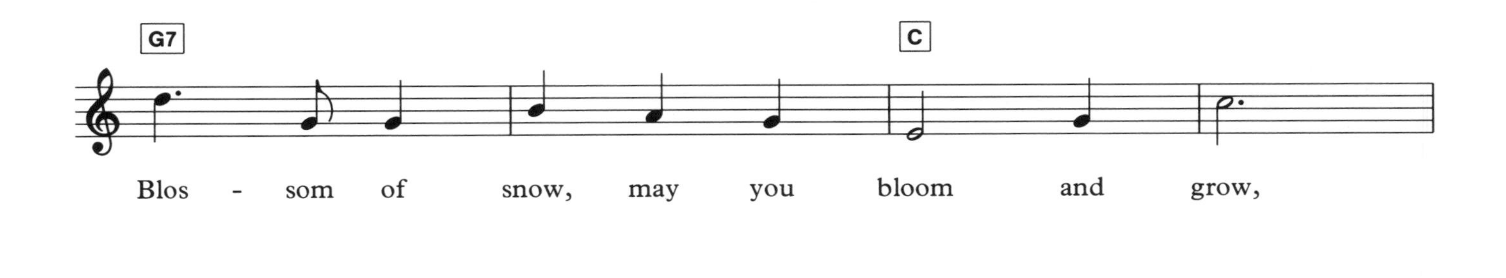
G7
C
Blos - som of snow, may you bloom and grow,

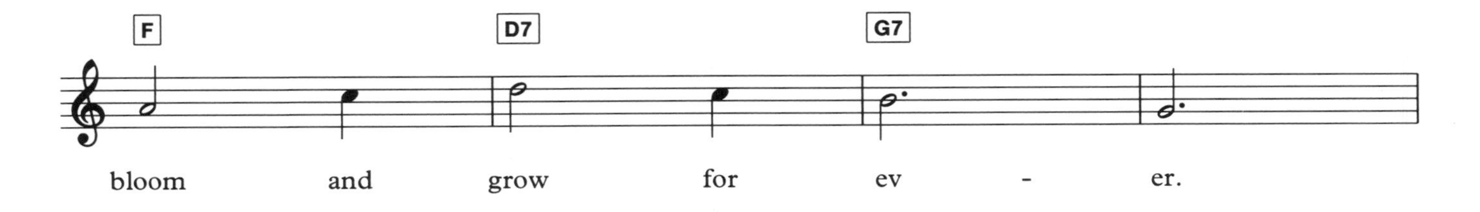
F
D7
G7
bloom and grow for ev - er.

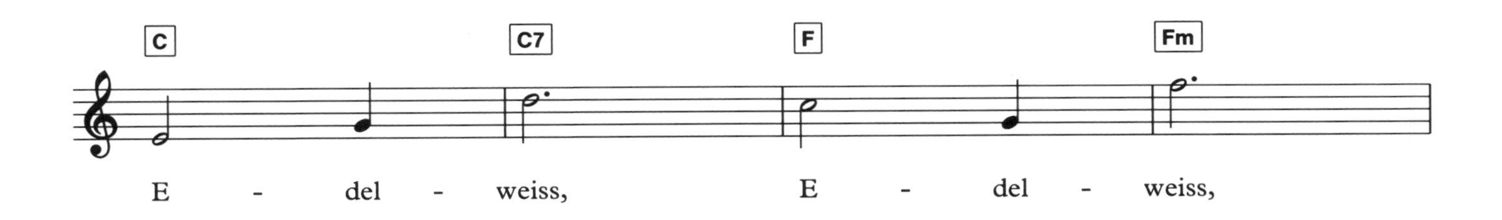
C
C7
F
Fm
E - del - weiss, E - del - weiss,

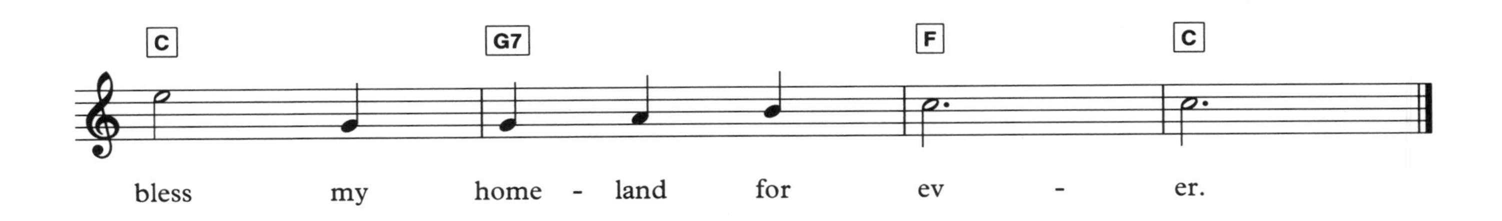
C
G7
F
C
bless my home - land for ev - er.

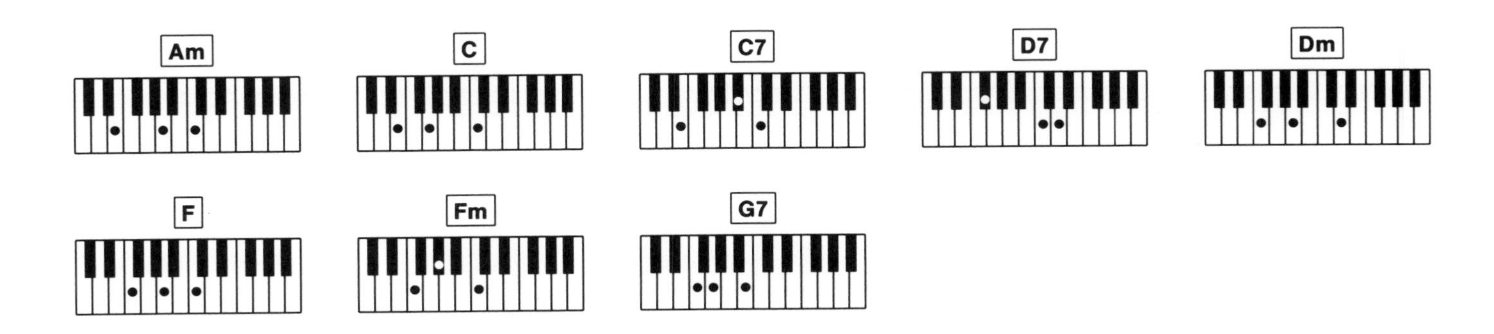
Am
C
C7
D7
Dm
F
Fm
G7

Ev'ry Time We Say Goodbye

Words & Music by Cole Porter

Suggested Registration: Strings
Rhythm: Soft Rock
Tempo: ♩ = 84

Am A7 Dm G7 C Dm
air of spring a - bout it, I can hear
E♭ G7 C F Fm
a lark some - where, be - gin to sing a - bout it.
E♭G♭A
C E♭dim Dm G7 C7 F
There's no love song fi - ner, but how strange, the change from
E♭G♭B♭
Fm C Em E♭m Dm G7 C
ma-jor to mi - nor, ev - 'ry time we say good - bye.

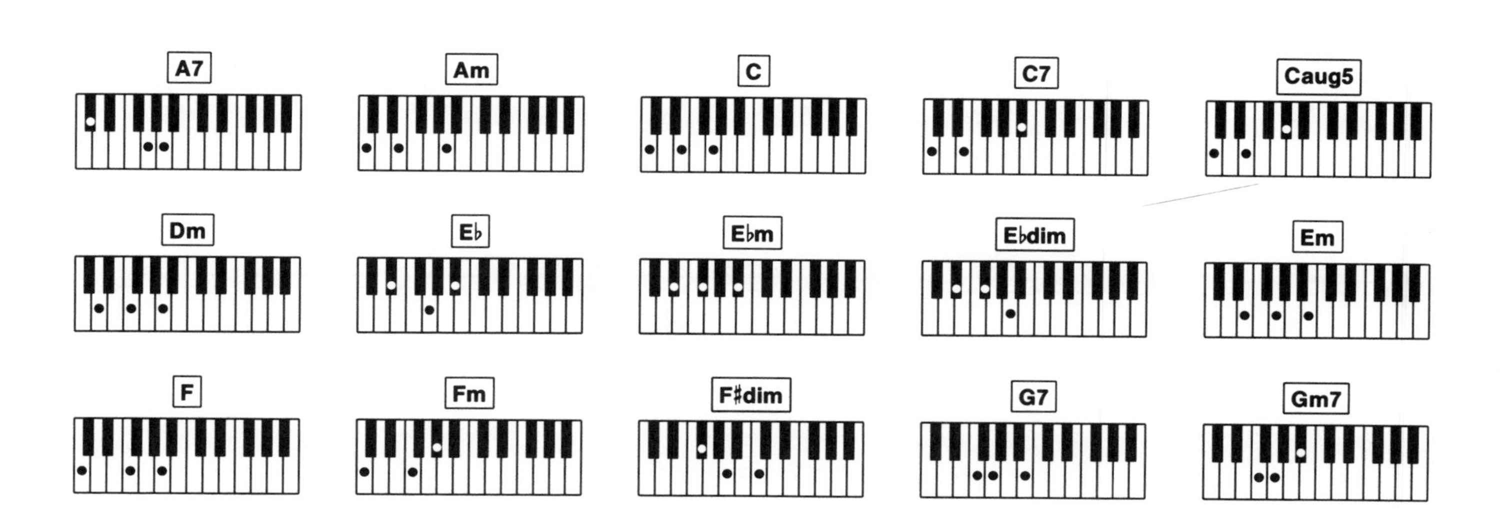
A7
Am
C
C7
Caug5
Dm
E♭
E♭m
E♭dim
Em
F
Fm
F♯dim
G7
Gm7

I Only Have Eyes For You

Words by Al Dubin
Music by Harry Warren

Suggested Registration: Strings
Rhythm: Soft Rock
Tempo: ♩ = 92

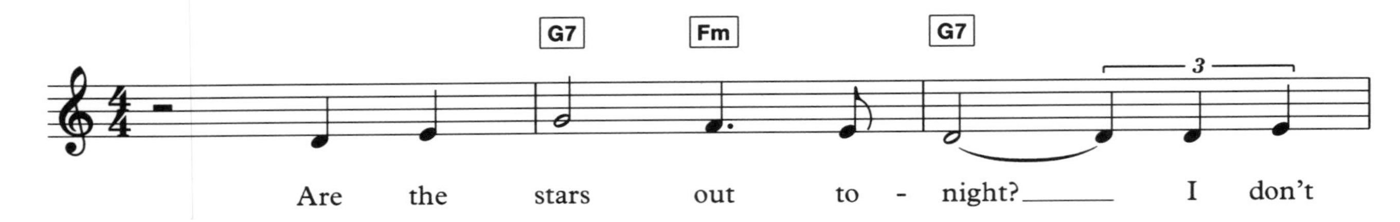

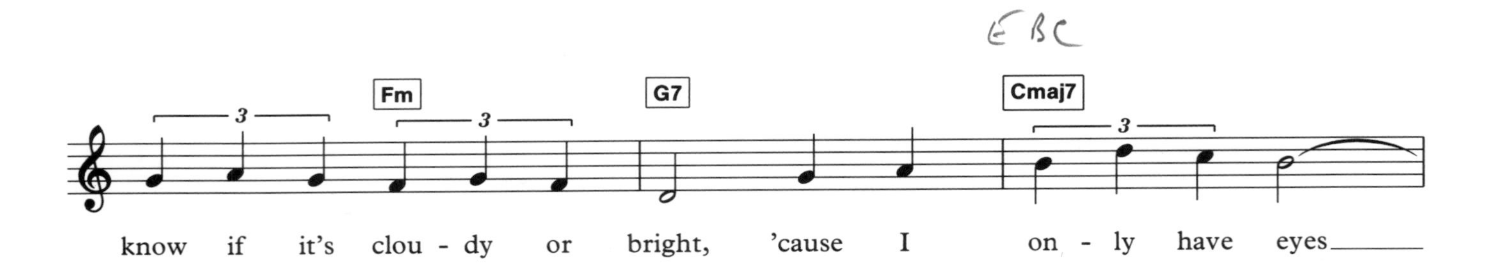

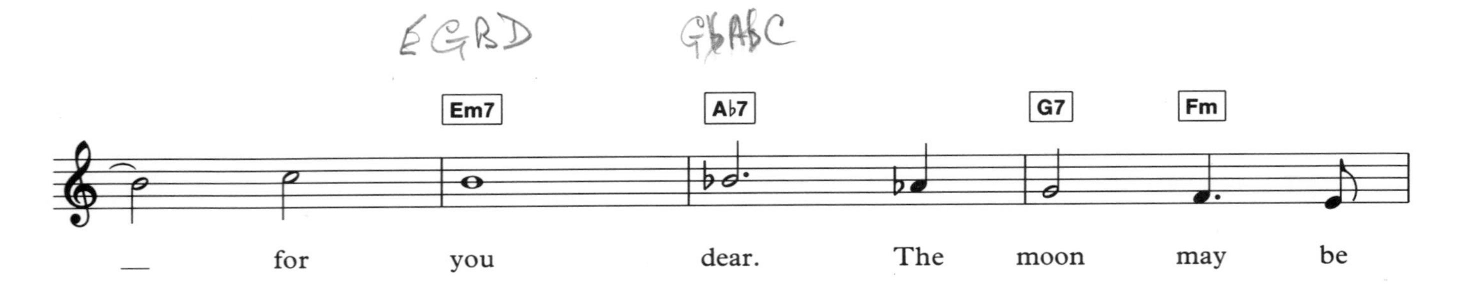

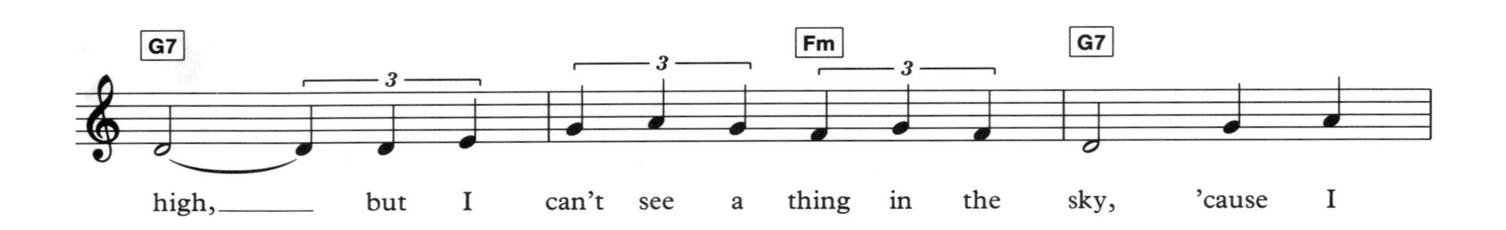

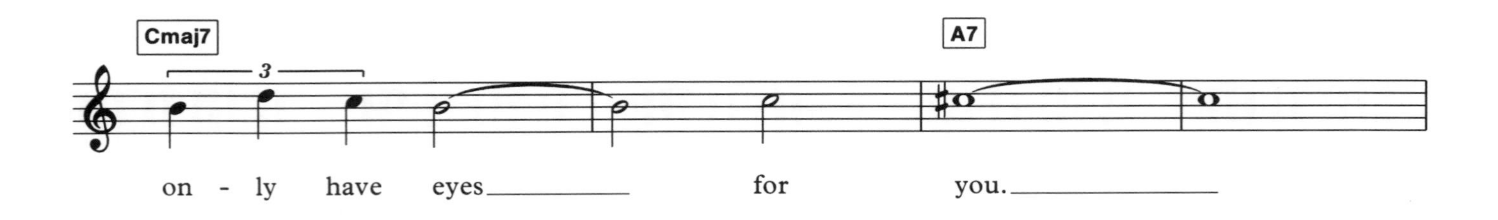

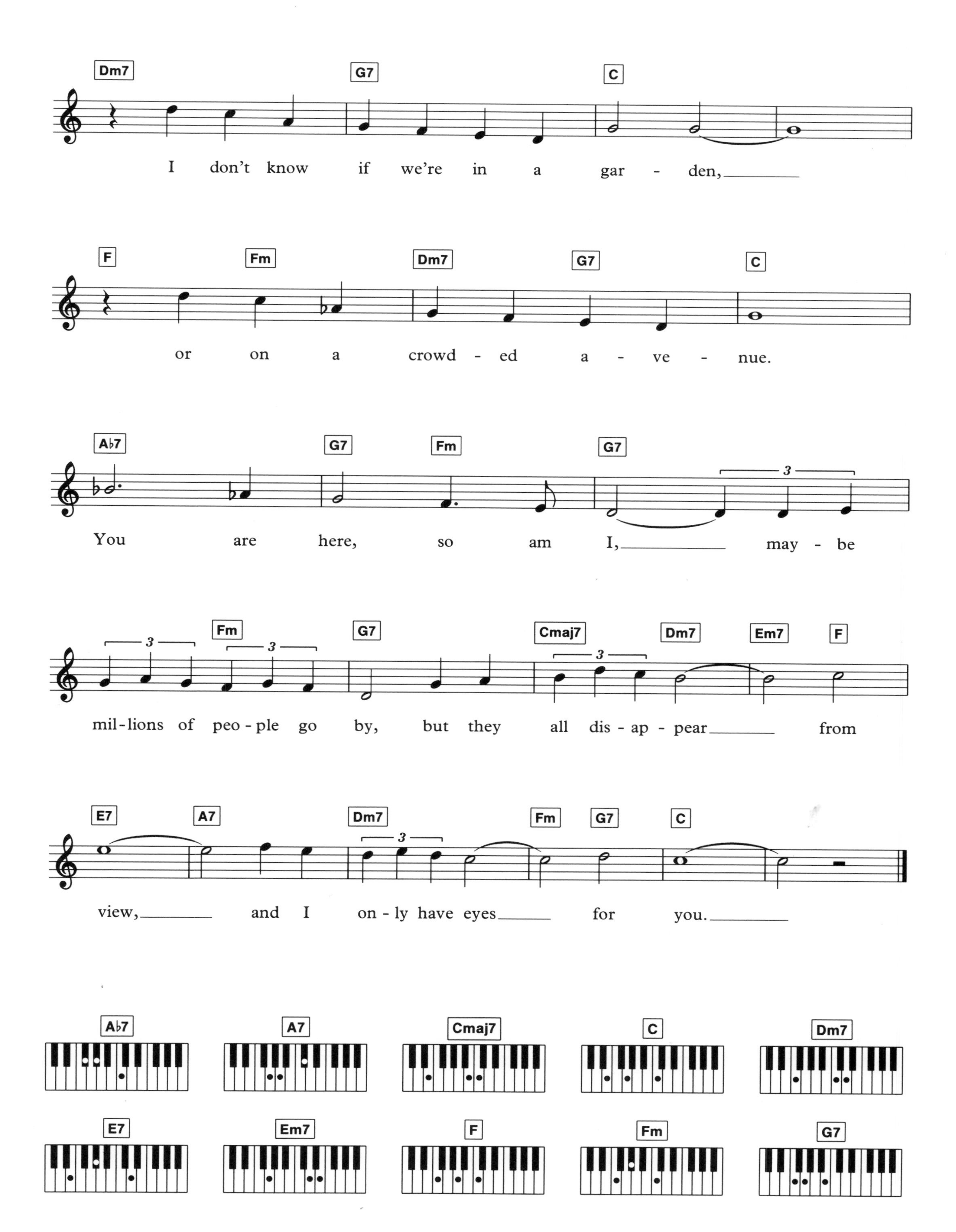
Dm7 G7 C
I don't know if we're in a gar - den,
F Fm Dm7 G7 C
or on a crowd - ed a - ve - nue.
A♭7 G7 Fm G7
You are here, so am I, may - be
Fm G7 Cmaj7 Dm7 Em7 F
mil-lions of peo-ple go by, but they all dis - ap - pear from
E7 A7 Dm7 Fm G7 C
view, and I on - ly have eyes for you.
A♭7
A7
Cmaj7
C
Dm7
E7
Em7
F
Fm
G7

I Whistle A Happy Tune

Words by Oscar Hammerstein II
Music by Richard Rodgers

Suggested Registration: Clarinet
Rhythm: Swing
Tempo: ♩ = 154

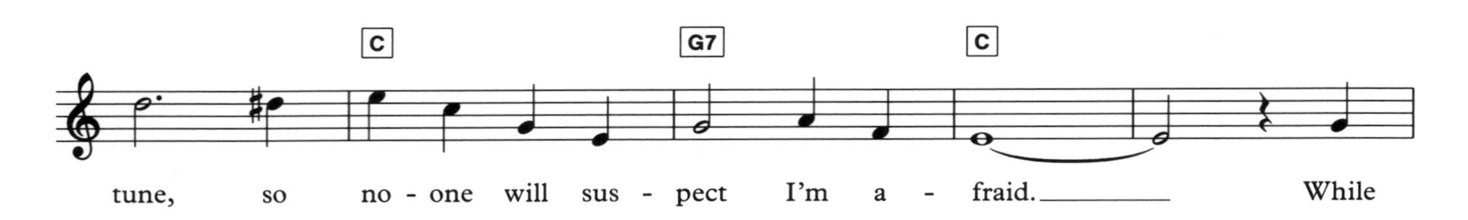

A♭
C
-sult of this de - cep - tion is ve - ry strange to
G
G♯dim
tell, for when I fool the peo - ple I fear, I
Am
D7
G7
C
fool my - self as well. I whis - tle a hap - py
F
tune, and ev - 'ry sin - gle time, the
G7
C
hap - pi - ness in the tune con - vin - ces me that
G7
C
I'm not a - fraid.
A♭
Am
C
D7
F
G
G7
G♯dim

Keep The Home Fires Burning

Words by Lena Guilbert Ford
Music by Ivor Novello

Suggested Registration: French Horn
Rhythm: March
Tempo: ♩ = 104

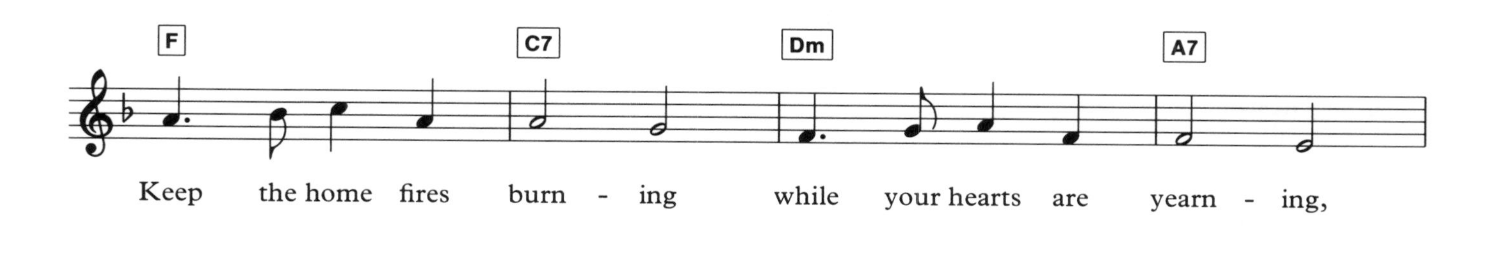
F
C7
Dm
A7
Keep the home fires burn - ing while your hearts are yearn - ing,

B♭
F
G7
C7
though your lads are far a - way, they dream of home.

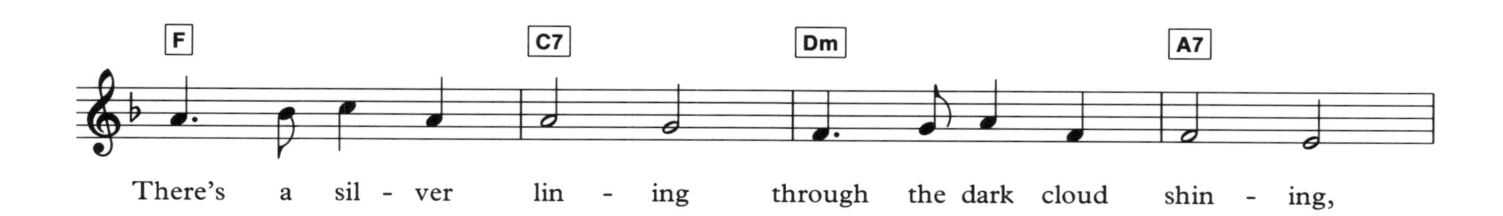
F
C7
Dm
A7
There's a sil - ver lin - ing through the dark cloud shin - ing,

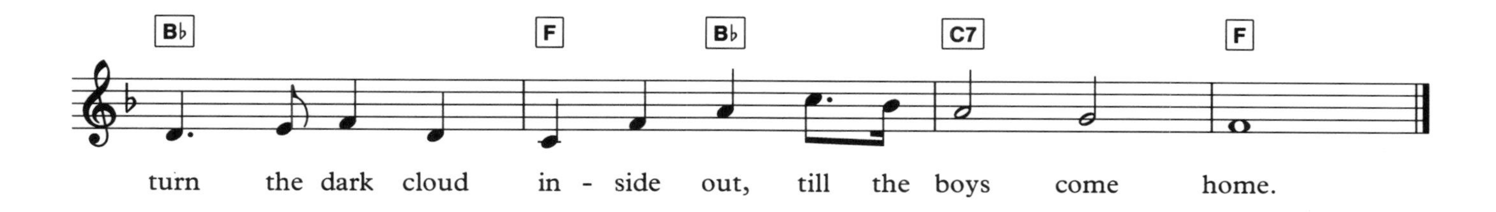
B♭
F
B♭
C7
F
turn the dark cloud in - side out, till the boys come home.

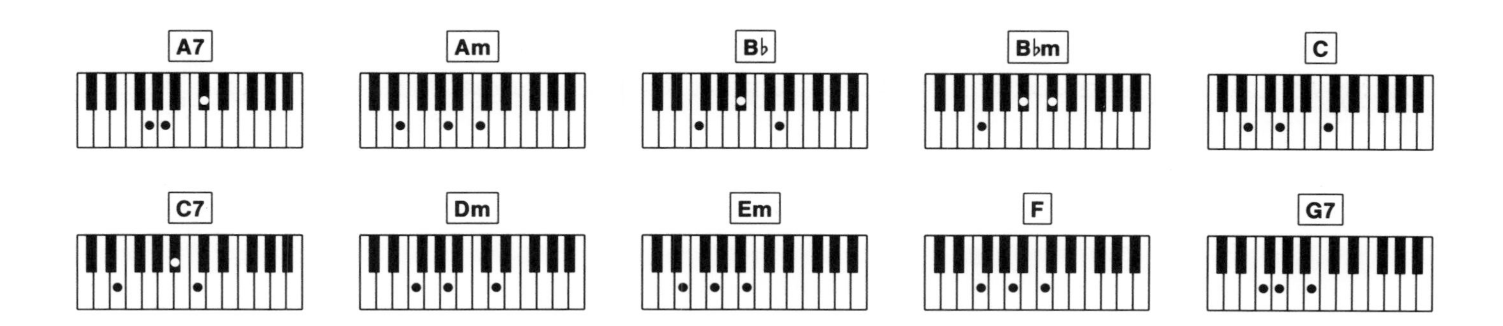
A7
Am
B♭
B♭m
C
C7
Dm
Em
F
G7

Let's Do It (Let's Fall In Love)

Words & Music by Cole Porter

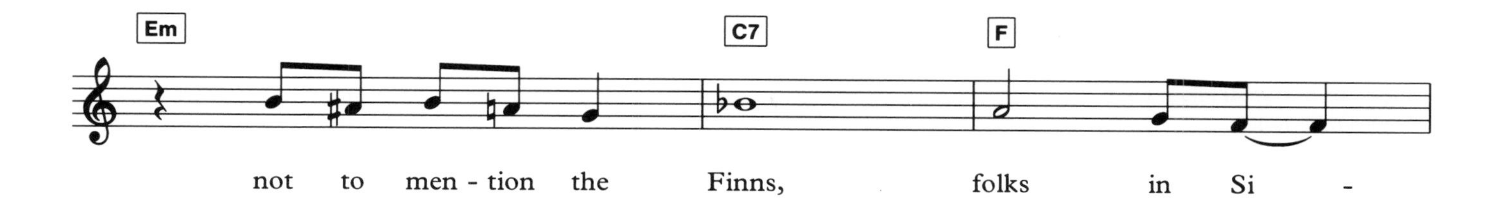
Em
C7
F
not to men - tion the Finns, folks in Si -

B♭
E♭
G7
- am do it,
think of Si - am - ese twins. Some Ar - gen -

C
G7
C
- tines with - out means do it,
peo - ple say in Bos - ton ev - en

F
C
Am
Dm
G7
C
Fm
C
beans do it,
let's do it,
let's fall in love.

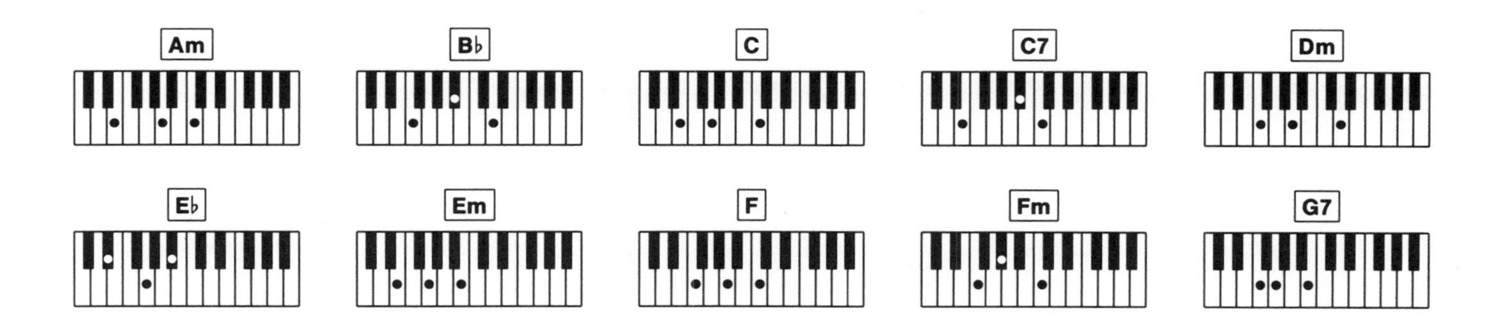
Am
B♭
C
C7
Dm
E♭
Em
F
Fm
G7

Love And Marriage

Words by Sammy Cahn
Music by James Van Heusen

Suggested Registration: Clarinet
Rhythm: Swing
Tempo: ♩ = 112

Eb7
Ab
it's an il - lu - sion, try, try,
C
G7
try and you will on - ly come to this con - clu - sion.
C
G7
C7
Love and mar - riage, love and mar - riage, go to - ge - ther like a
F
Fm
C
E
F
horse and car - riage, Dad was told by Mo - ther, you
Cdim
C
Cdim
C
Cdim
C
G7
C
can't have one, you can't have one, you can't have one, with-out the oth - er.

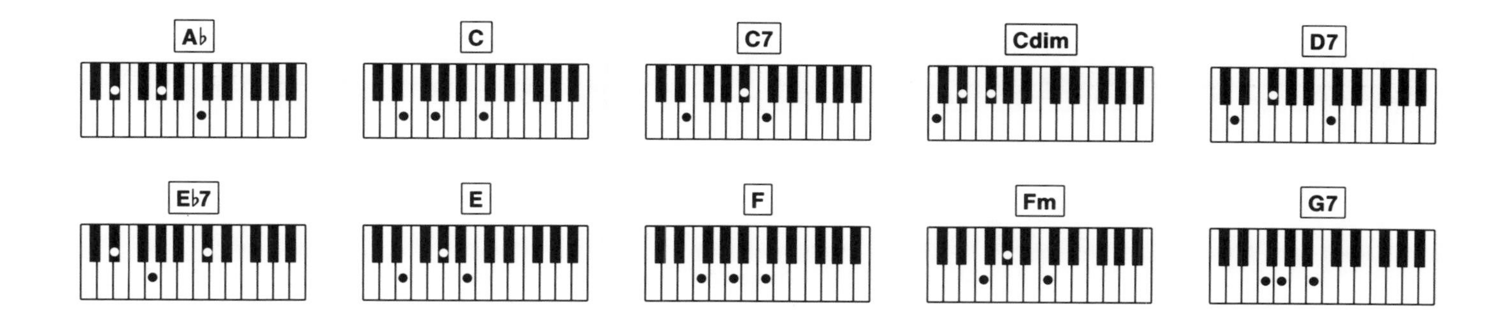

Ab
C
C7
Cdim
D7
Eb7
E
F
Fm
G7

On The Street Where You Live

Words by Alan Jay Lerner
Music by Frederick Loewe

Suggested Registration: Strings
Rhythm: Swing
Tempo: ♩ = 144

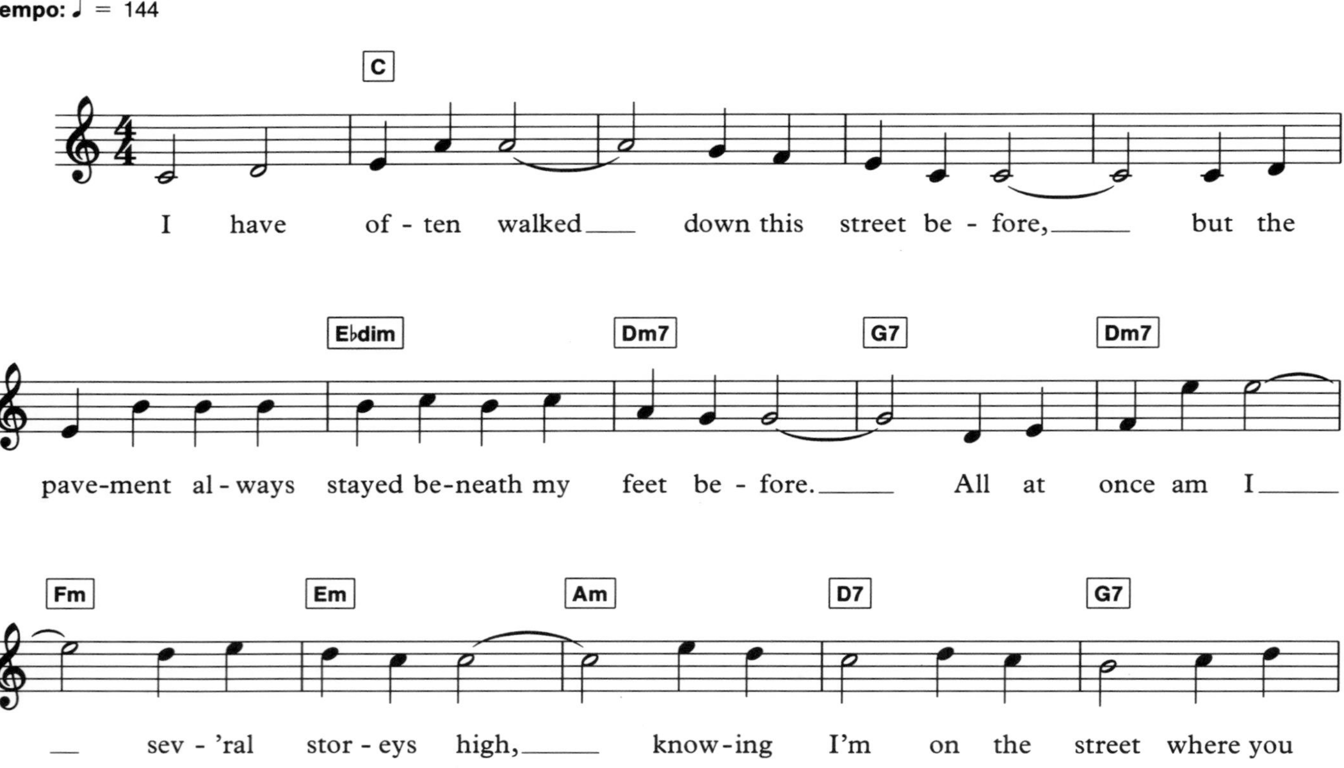

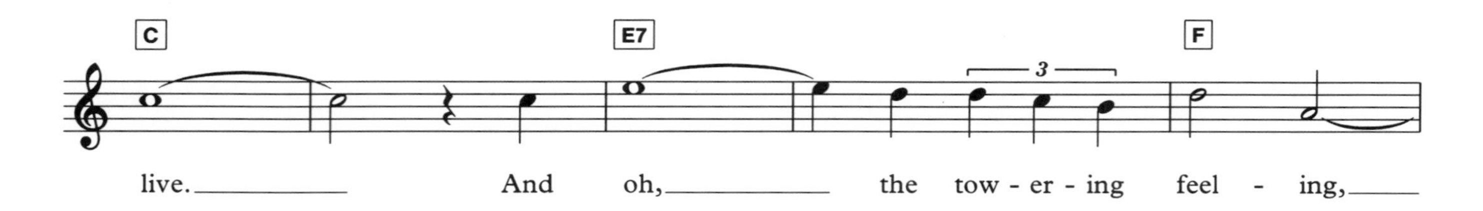

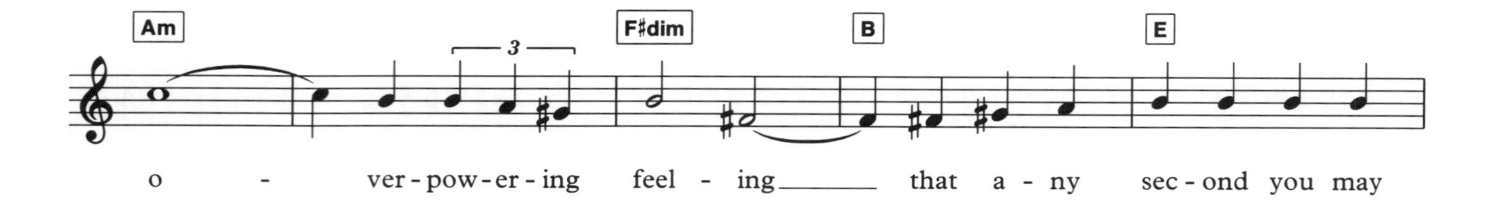

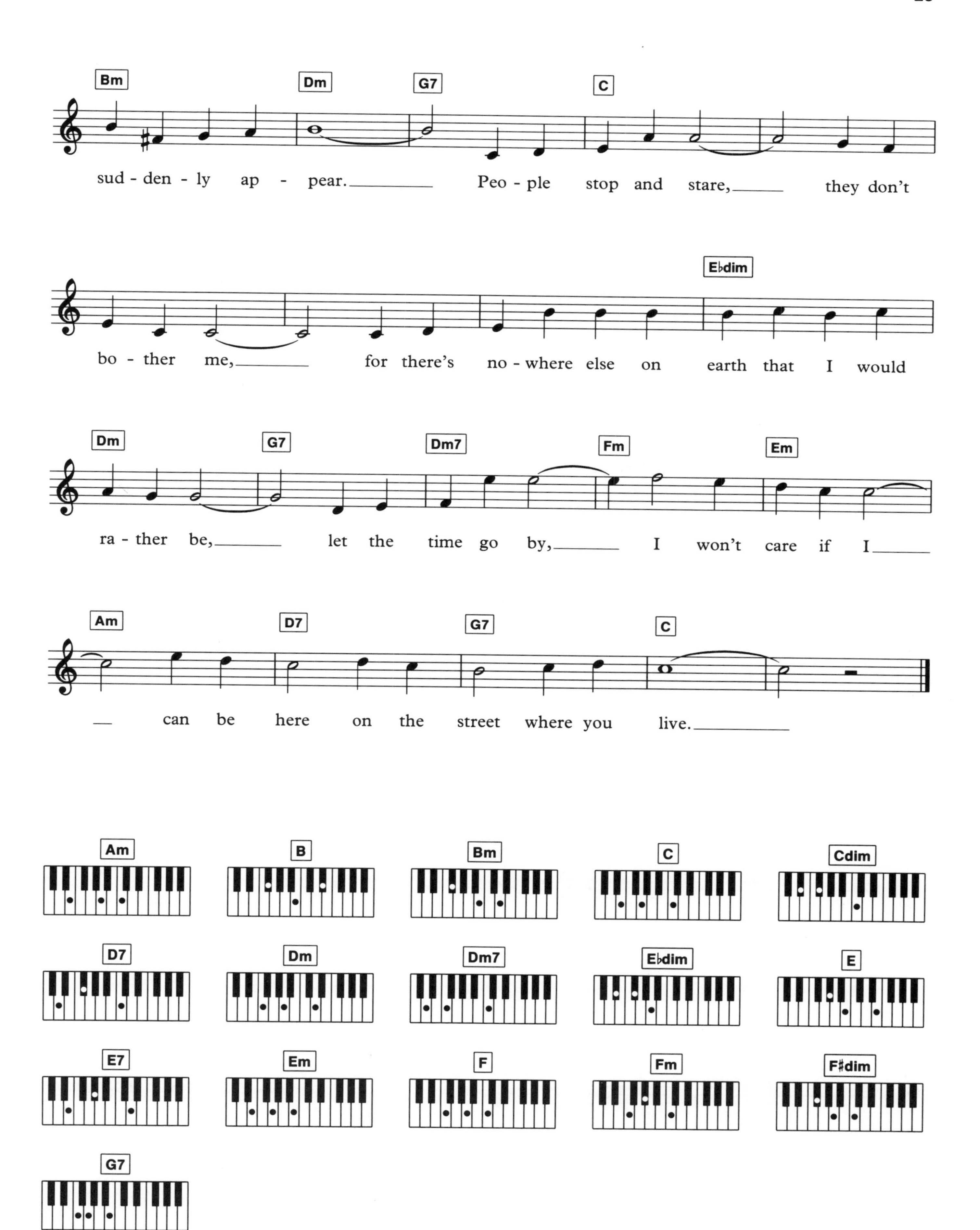
Bm
Dm
G7
C
sud - den - ly ap - pear. Peo - ple stop and stare, they don't
E♭dim
bo - ther me, for there's no - where else on earth that I would
Dm
G7
Dm7
Fm
Em
ra - ther be, let the time go by, I won't care if I
Am
D7
G7
C
can be here on the street where you live.
Am
B
Bm
C
Cdim
D7
Dm
Dm7
E♭dim
E
E7
Em
F
Fm
F♯dim
G7

SEPTEMBER SONG

Words by Maxwell Anderson / Music by Kurt Weill

Suggested Registration: Jazz Guitar
Rhythm: Swing
Tempo: ♩ = 94

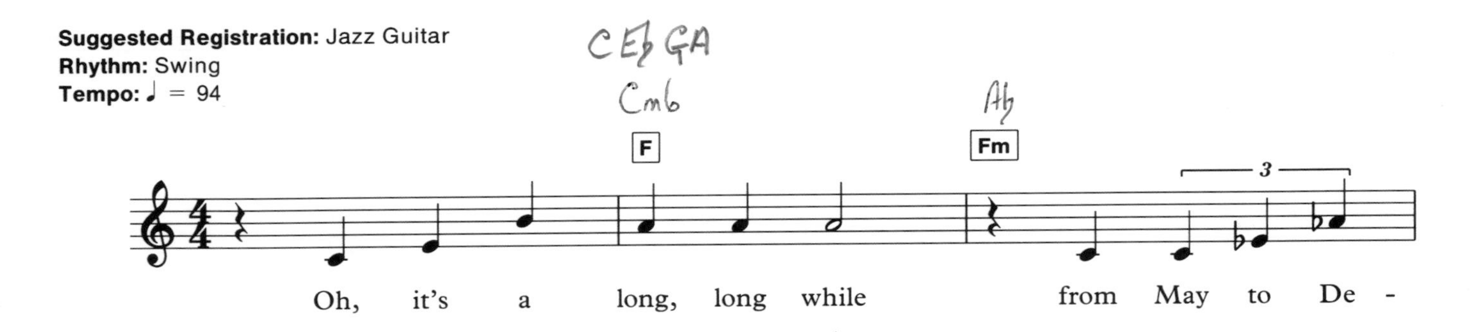

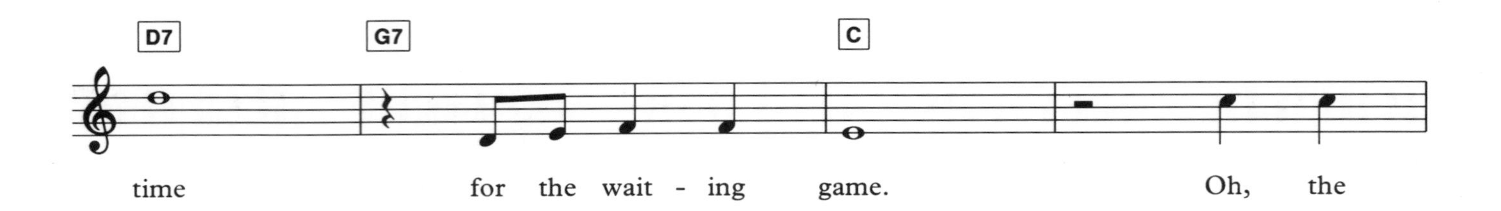

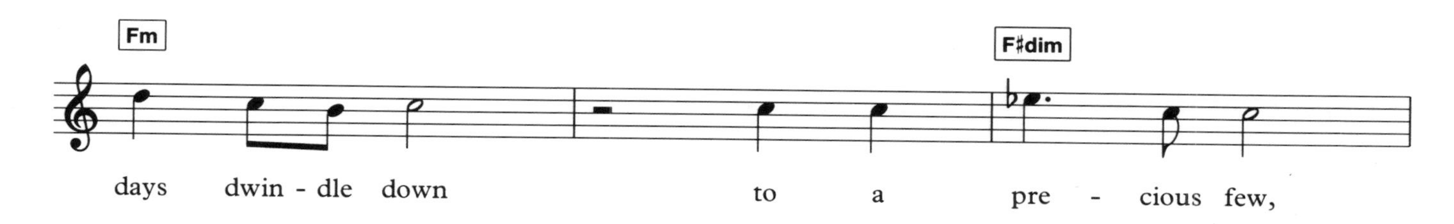
G♭AC
Fm
F♯dim
days dwin - dle down to a pre - cious few,

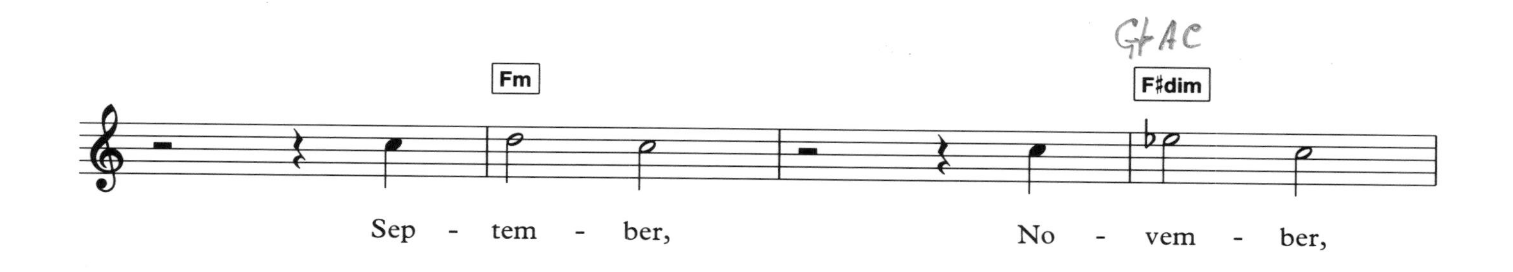
G♭AC
Fm
F♯dim
Sep - tem - ber, No - vem - ber,

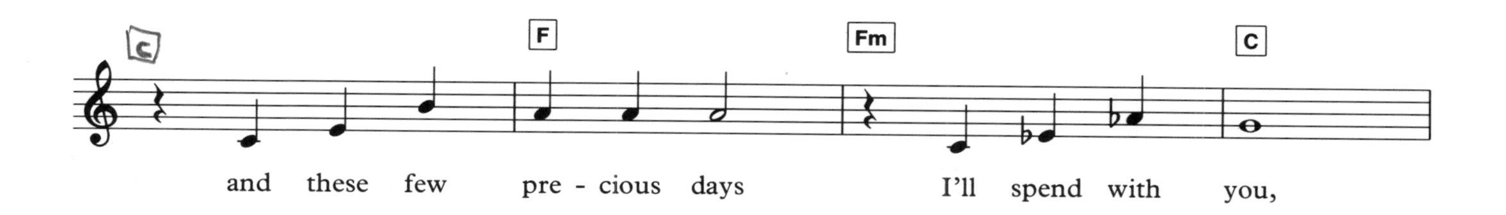
C
F
Fm
C
and these few pre - cious days I'll spend with you,

FGCD.
D7
G7sus4
C
these pre - cious days I'll spend with you.

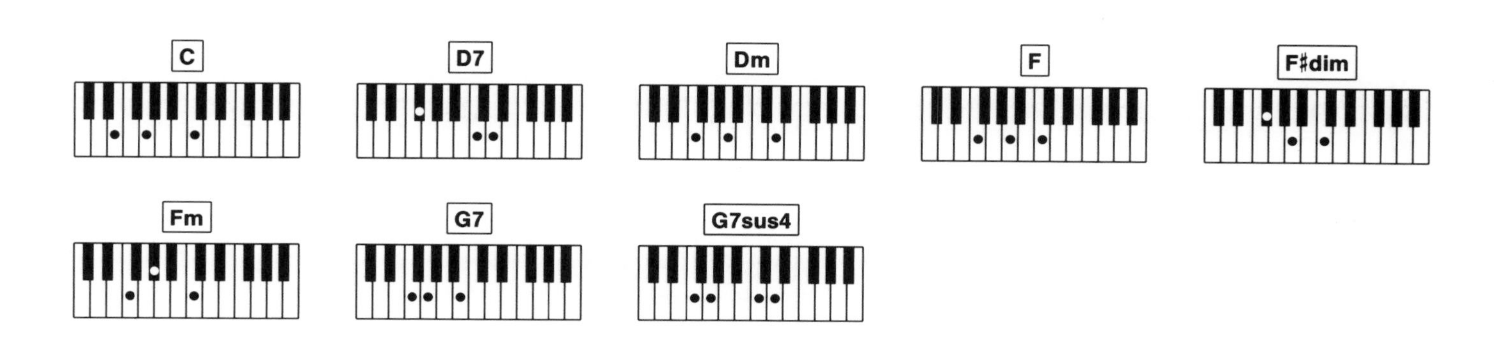
C
D7
Dm
F
F♯dim
Fm
G7
G7sus4

Shall We Dance?

Words by Oscar Hammerstein II
Music by Richard Rodgers

Suggested Registration: Vibraphone
Rhythm: Swing
Tempo: ♩ = 160

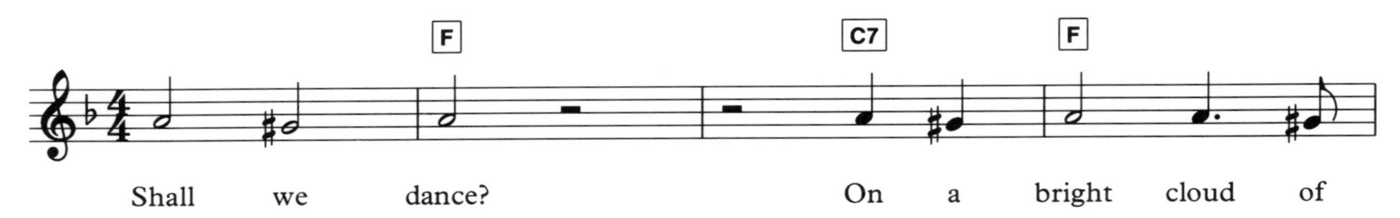

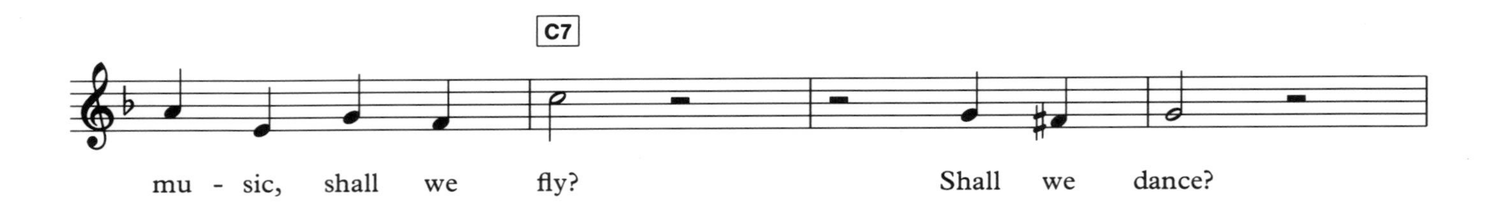

F
-ge - ther, with our arms a - round each oth - er, and shall

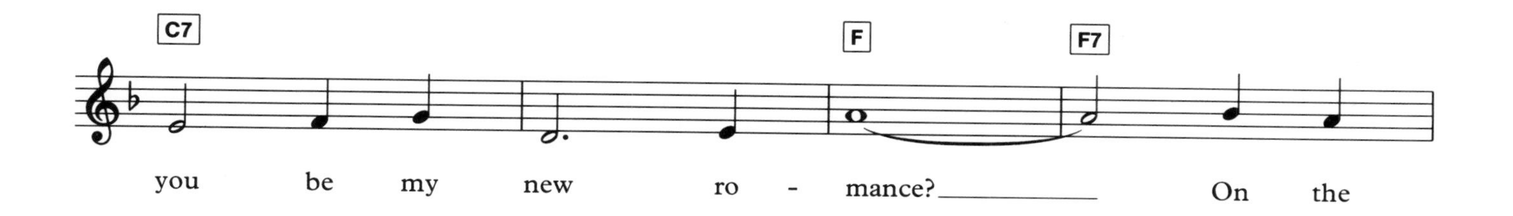
C7
F
F7
you be my new ro - mance?
On the

B♭
F
clear un - der - stand - ing that this kind of thing can

D7
Gm7
C7
F
hap-pen, shall we dance? Shall we dance? Shall we dance?

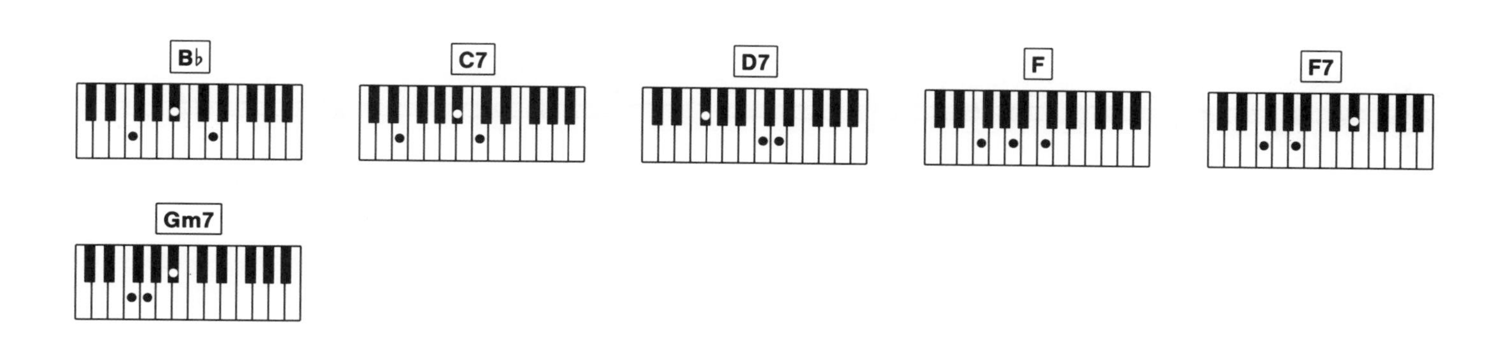
B♭
C7
D7
F
F7
Gm7

Some Enchanted Evening

Words by Oscar Hammerstein II
Music by Richard Rodgers

Suggested Registration: Strings
Rhythm: Soft Rock
Tempo: ♩ = 78

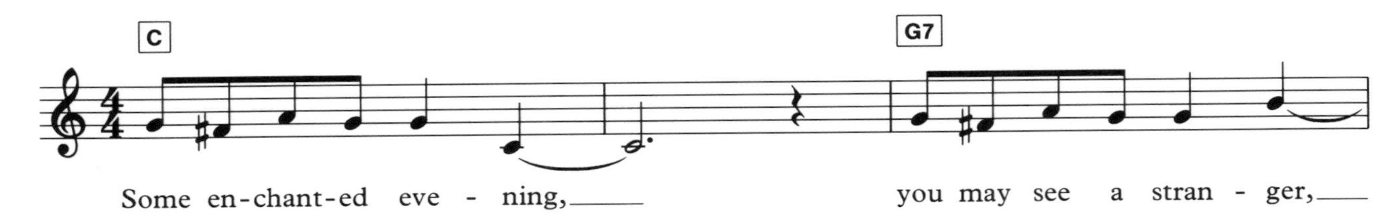

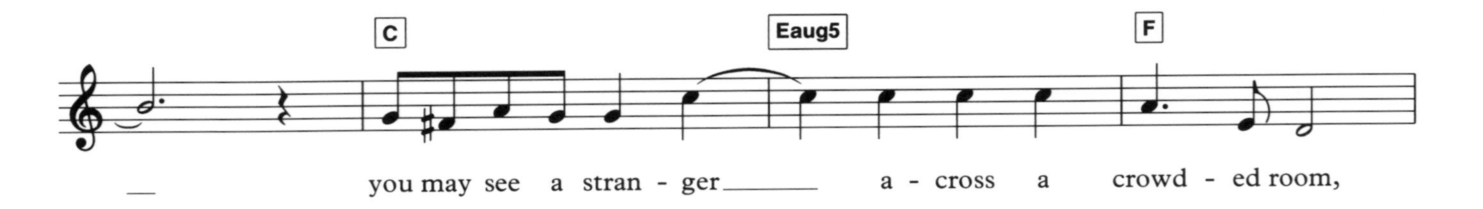

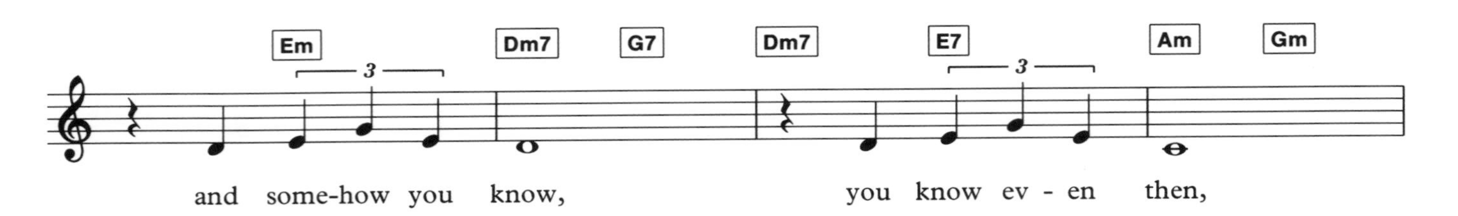

Eaug5
F
Em
Dm7
G7
3
— a - cross a crowd - ed room, then fly to her side,
Dm7
E7
Am
Gm
F
Em
and make her your own, or all through your
Dm7
G7
C
life you may dream all a - lone.
G7
C
G7
C
G7
C
Once you have found her, ne - ver let her go, once you have found her,
Dm7
C
ne - ver let her go.
Am
C
Dm7
E7
Eaug5
Em
F
G7
Gm

Someone To Watch Over Me

Music and Lyrics by George Gershwin and Ira Gershwin

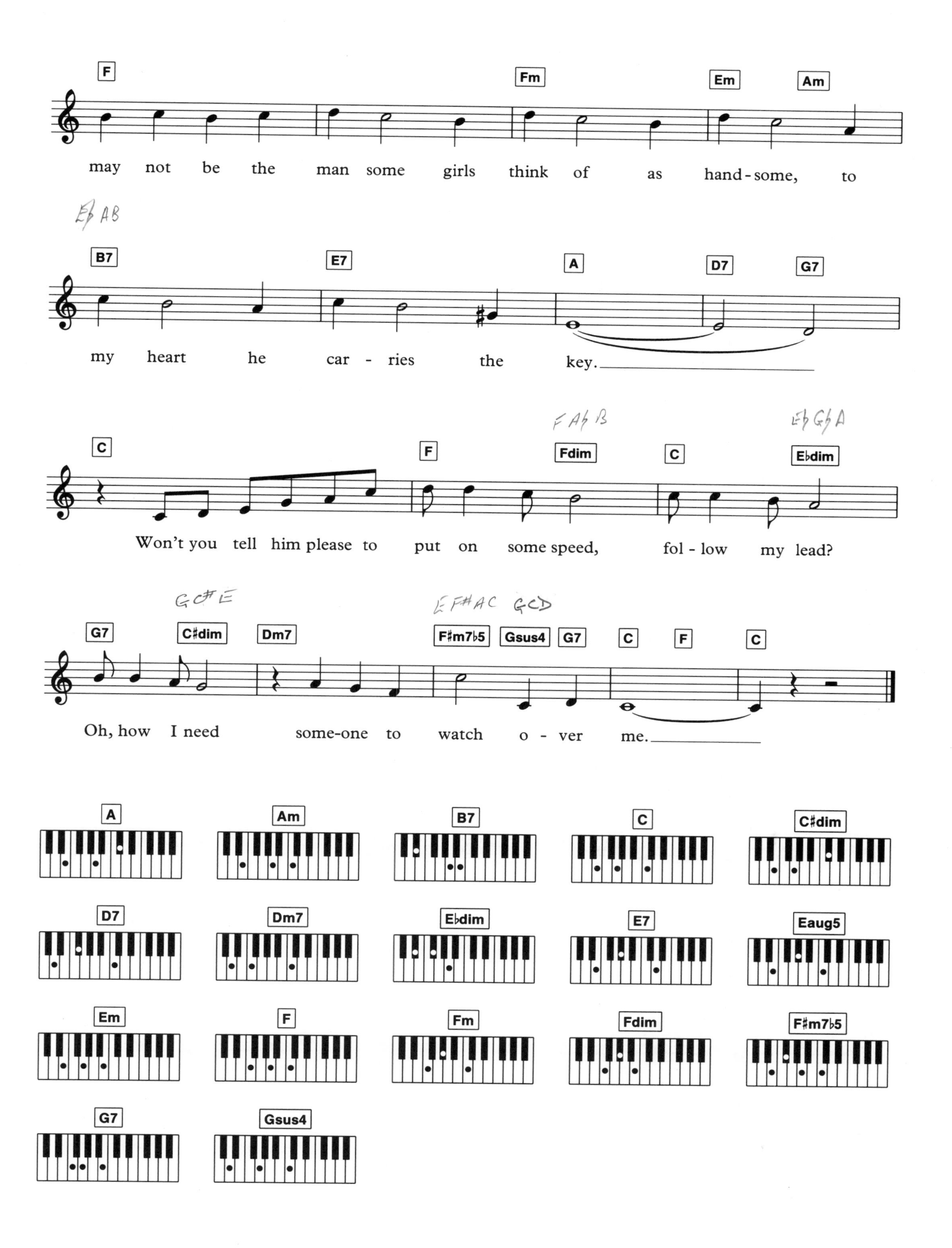
F
Fm
Em
Am
may not be the man some girls think of as hand - some, to
E♭ A B
B7
E7
A
D7
G7
my heart he car - ries the key.
F A♭ B
E♭ G♭ A
C
F
Fdim
C
E♭dim
Won't you tell him please to put on some speed, fol - low my lead?
G C♯ E
E F♯ A C
G C D
G7
C♯dim
Dm7
F♯m7♭5
Gsus4
G7
C
F
C
Oh, how I need some-one to watch o - ver me.
A
Am
B7
C
C♯dim
D7
Dm7
E♭dim
E7
Eaug5
Em
F
Fm
Fdim
F♯m7♭5
G7
Gsus4

They Can't Take That Away From Me

Music and Lyrics by George Gershwin and Ira Gershwin

Suggested Registration: Vibraphone
Rhythm: Swing
Tempo: ♩ = 112

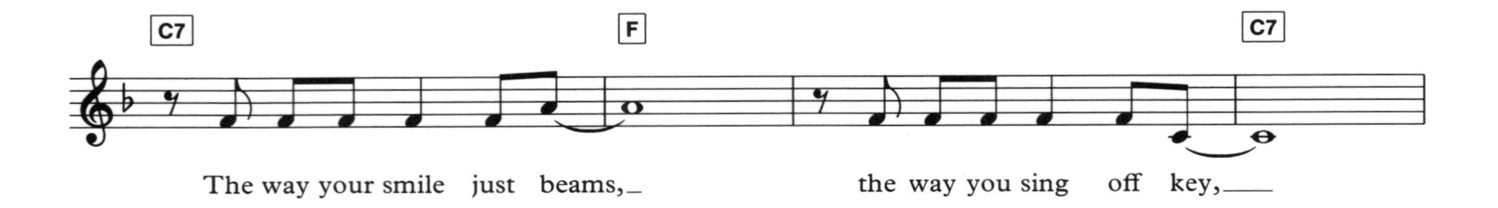

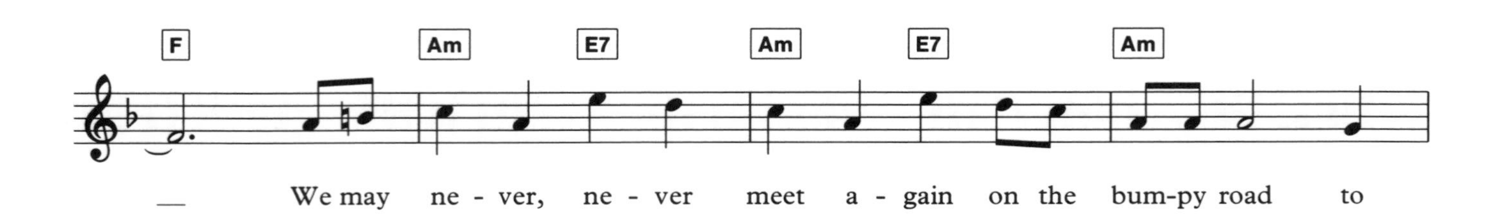

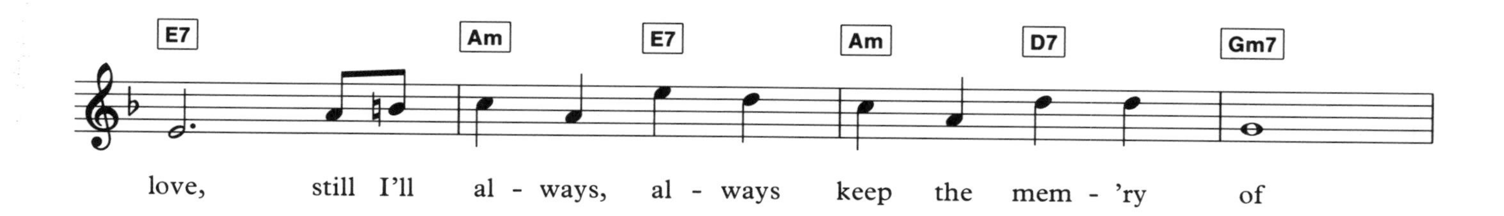
E7
Am
E7
Am
D7
Gm7
love, still I'll al - ways, al - ways keep the mem - 'ry of

C7
F
C7
the way you hold your knife,
the way we danced till three,

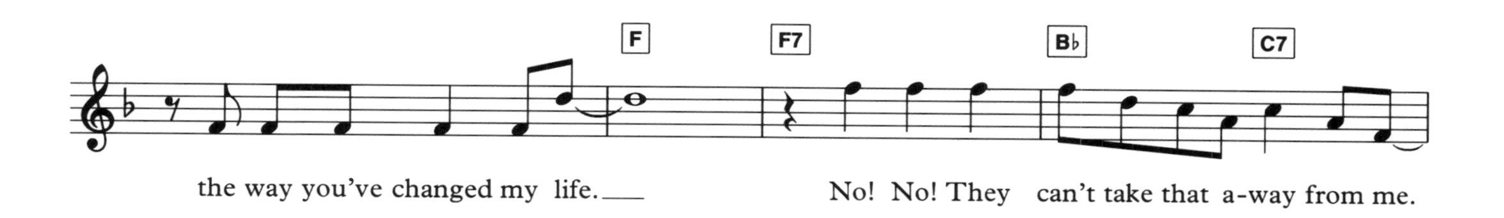
F
F7
B♭
C7
the way you've changed my life.
No! No! They can't take that a-way from me.

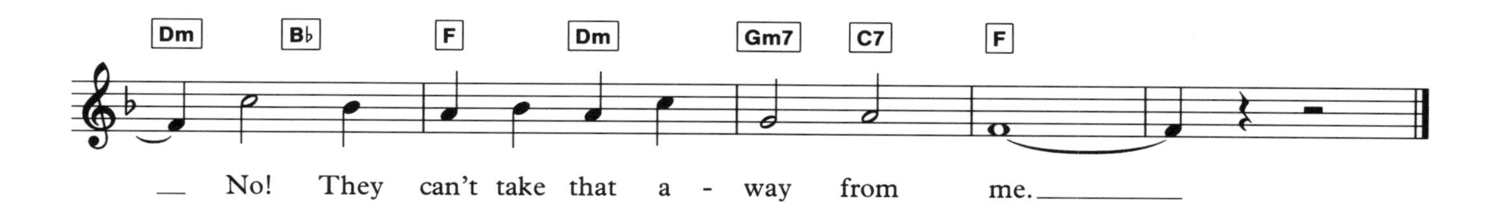
Dm
B♭
F
Dm
Gm7
C7
F
No! They can't take that a - way from me.

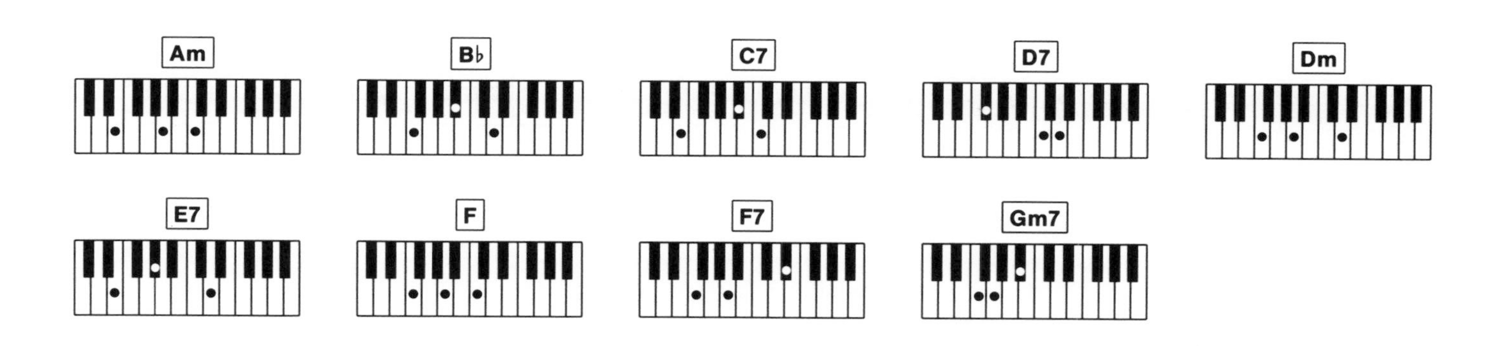
Am
B♭
C7
D7
Dm
E7
F
F7
Gm7

This Can't Be Love

Words by Lorenz Hart
Music by Richard Rodgers

Suggested Registration: Clarinet
Rhythm: Swing
Tempo: ♩ = 130

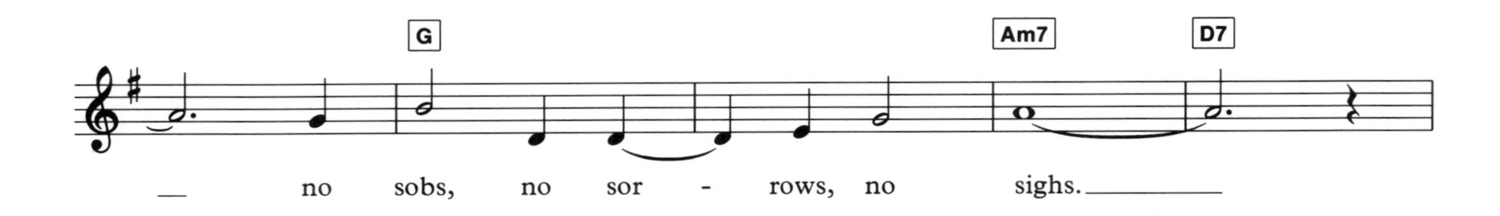

Em
Bm7
E7
beat, this is too sweet to

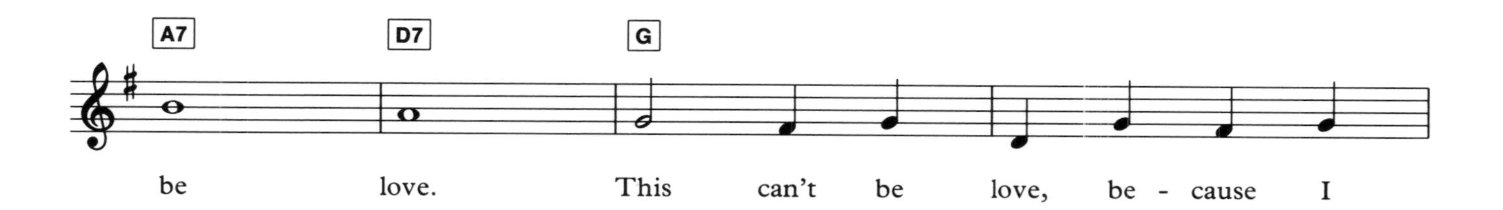
A7
D7
G
be love. This can't be love, be - cause I

C
G
feel so well, but I still love to look

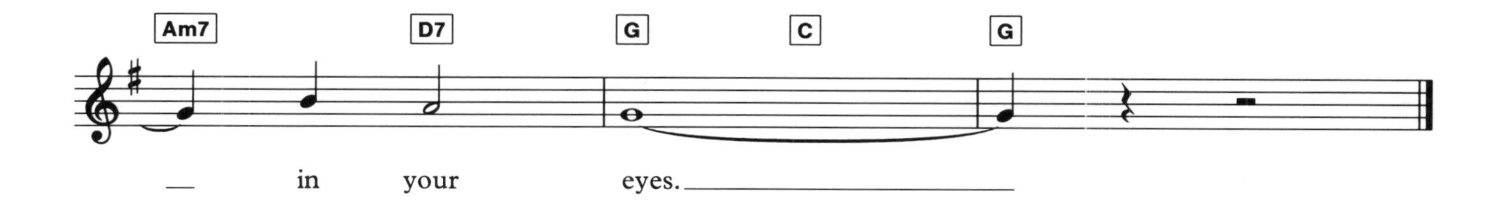
Am7
D7
G
C
G
in your eyes.

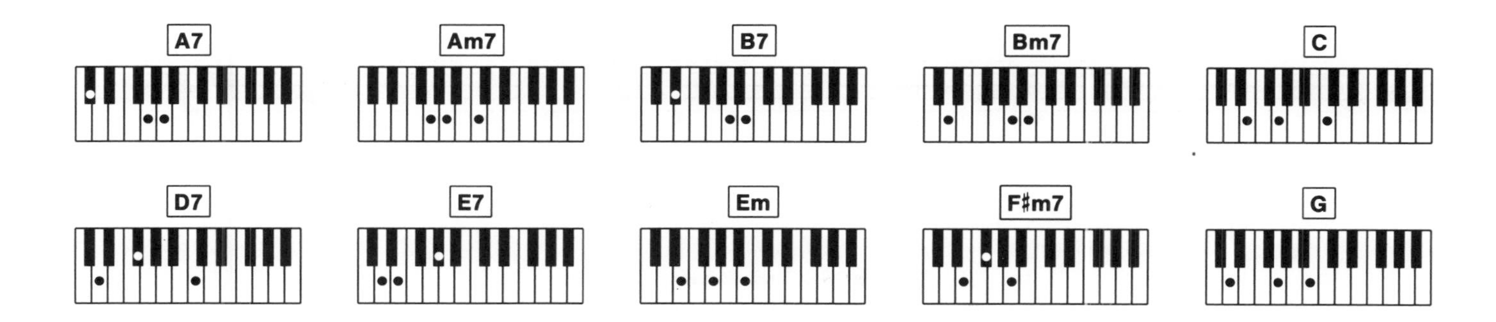
A7
Am7
B7
Bm7
C
D7
E7
Em
F♯m7
G

TIME AFTER TIME

Words by Sammy Cahn
Music by Jule Styne

Suggested Registration: Piano
Rhythm: Swing
Tempo: ♩ = 120

Dm7
G7
C
C7
show you've kept my love so young, so

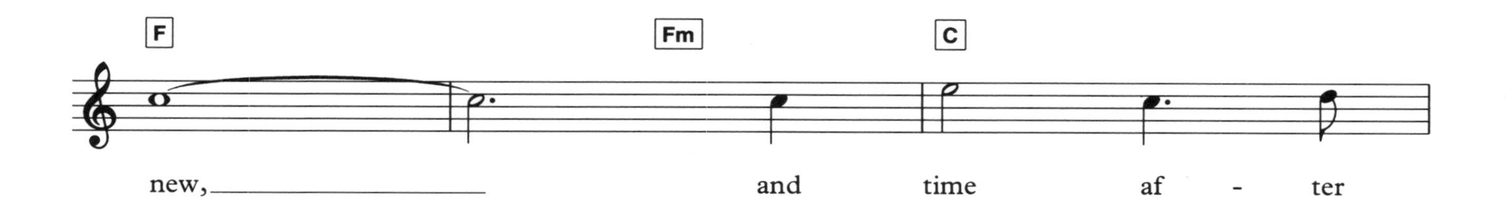
F
Fm
C
new, and time af - ter

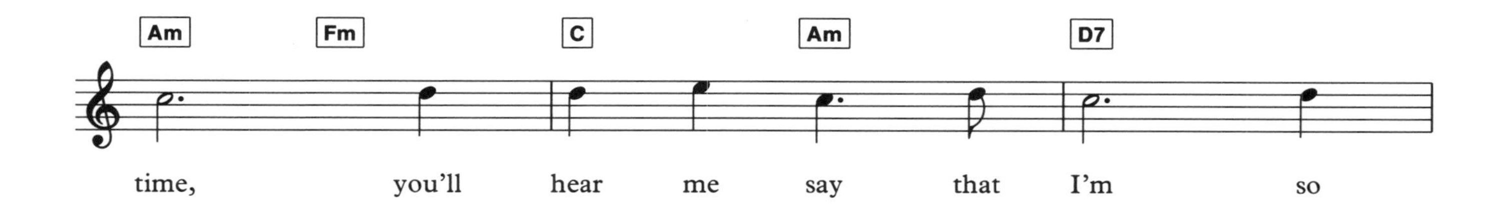
Am
Fm
C
Am
D7
time, you'll hear me say that I'm so

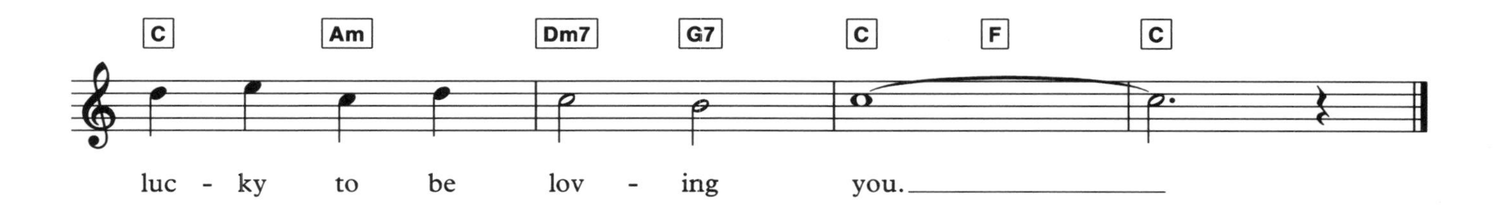
C
Am
Dm7
G7
C
F
C
luc - ky to be lov - ing you.

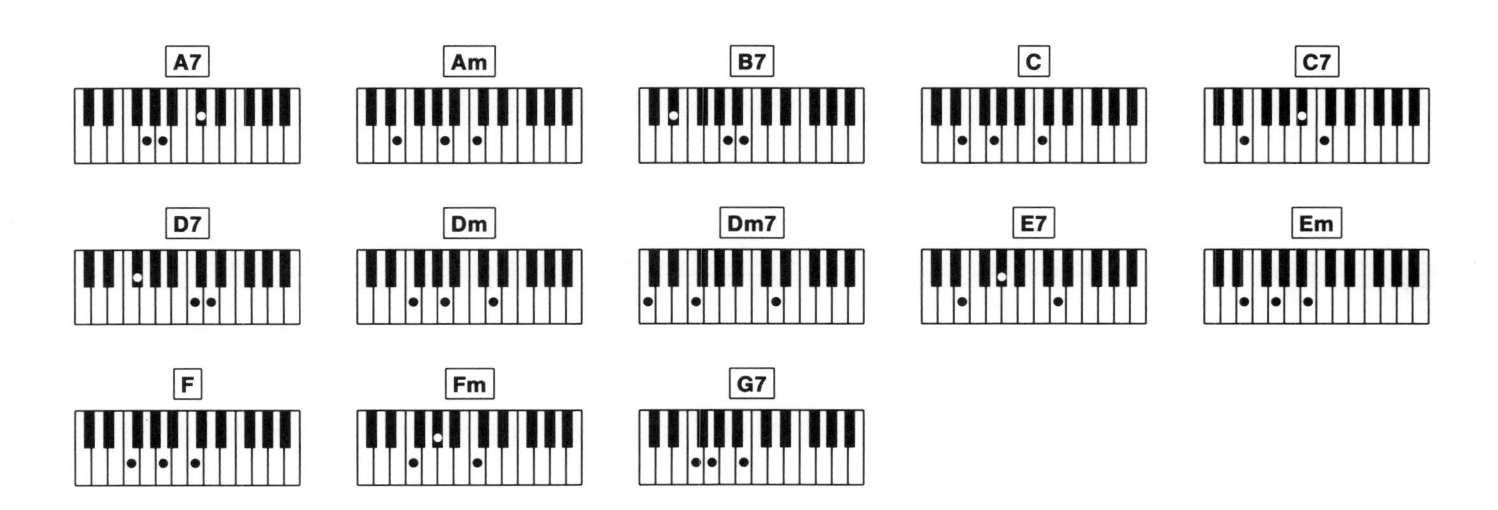
A7
Am
B7
C
C7
D7
Dm
Dm7
E7
Em
F
Fm
G7

We'll Gather Lilacs

Words & Music by Ivor Novello

Suggested Registration: Flute
Rhythm: Swing
Tempo: ♩ = 128

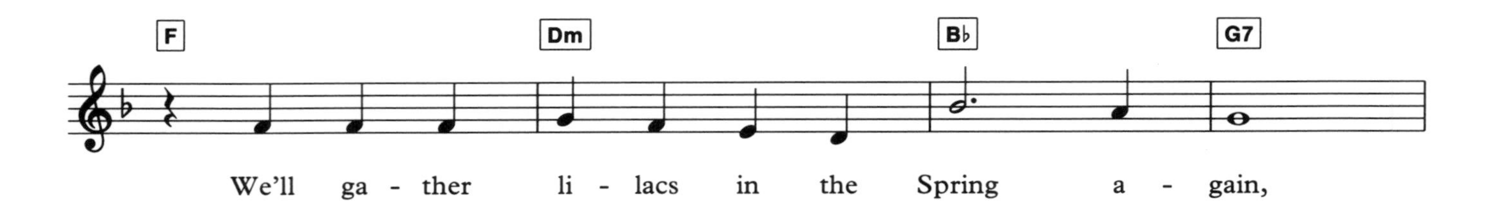

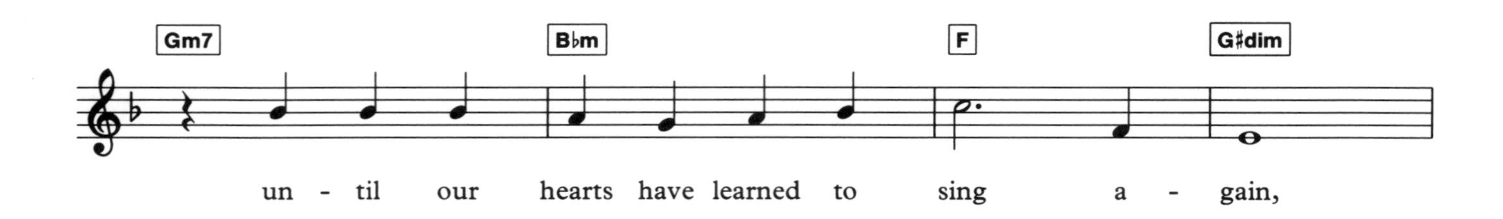

F
Dm
B♭
G7
And in the eve - ning by the fire - light's glow,

C7
F
D7
you'll hold me close and ne - ver let me go,

Gm7
B♭m
F
Am
your eyes will tell me all I want to know,

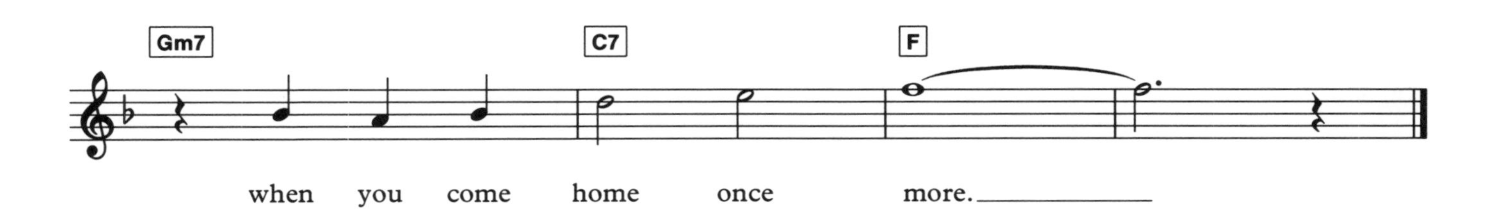
Gm7
C7
F
when you come home once more.

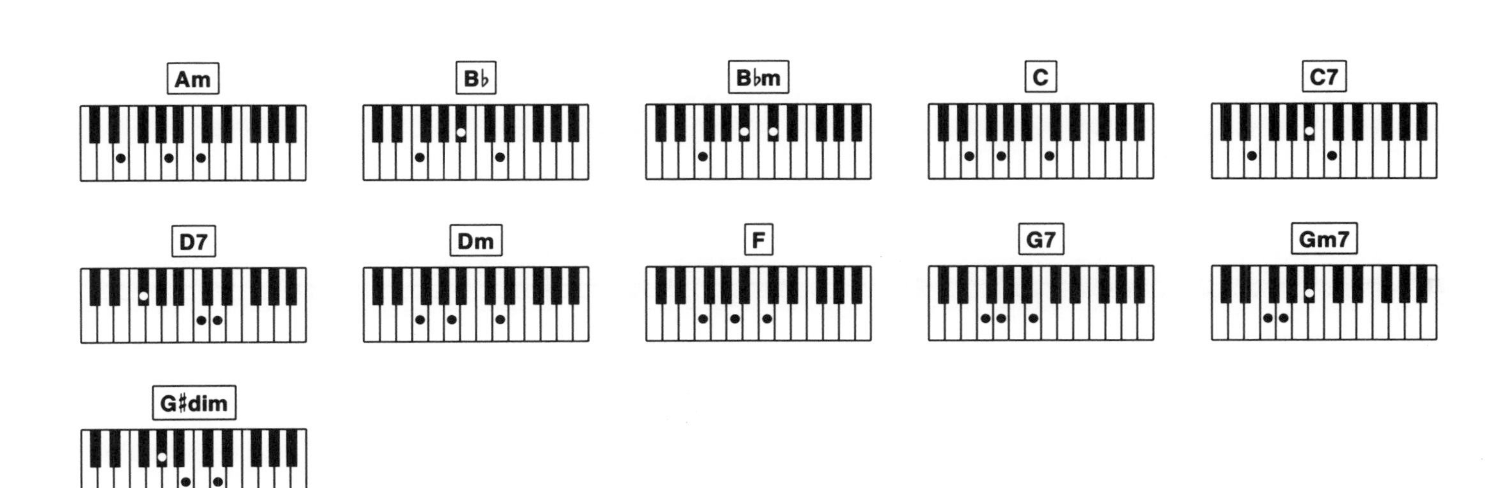
Am
B♭
B♭m
C
C7
D7
Dm
F
G7
Gm7
G♯dim

WHERE OR WHEN

Words by Lorenz Hart
Music by Richard Rodgers

Suggested Registration: Strings
Rhythm: Swing
Tempo: ♩ = 126

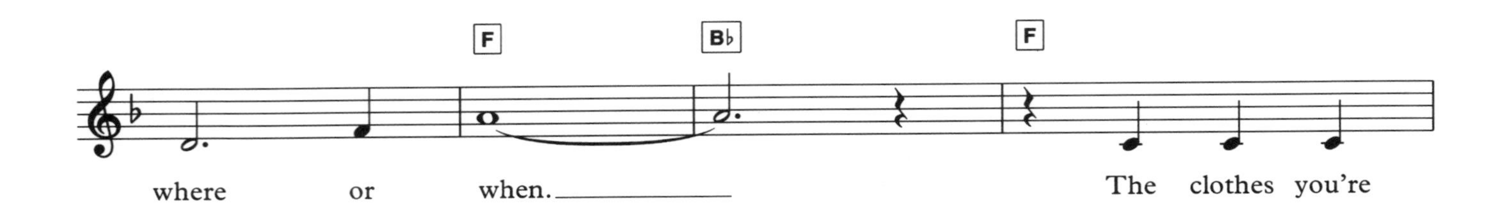

Dm
Gm7
G7
C7
seem to be hap - pen - ing a - gain,

F
Faug5
and so it seems that we have met be - fore, and

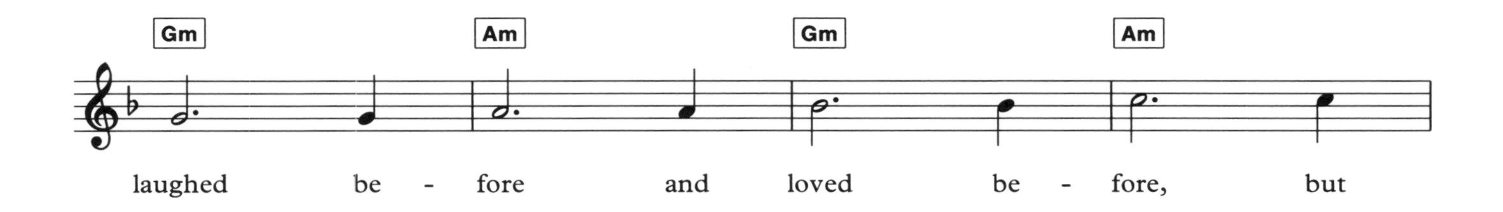
Gm
Am
Gm
Am
laughed be - fore and loved be - fore, but

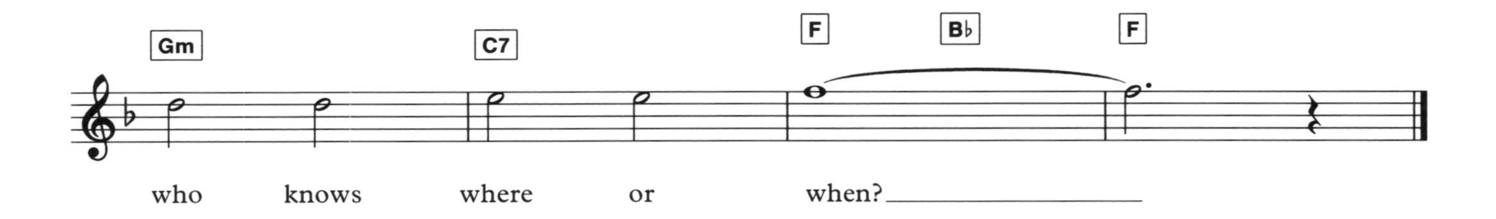
Gm
C7
F
B♭
F
who knows where or when?

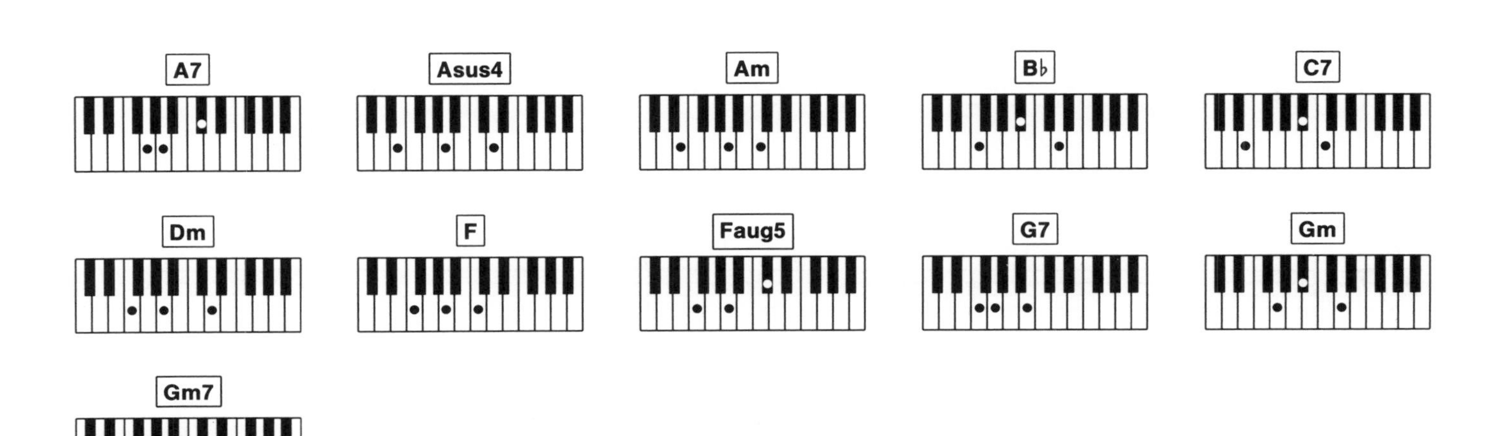
A7
Asus4
Am
B♭
C7
Dm
F
Faug5
G7
Gm
Gm7

You Do Something To Me

Words & Music by Cole Porter

Suggested Registration: Vibraphone
Rhythm: Swing
Tempo: ♩ = 160

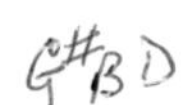

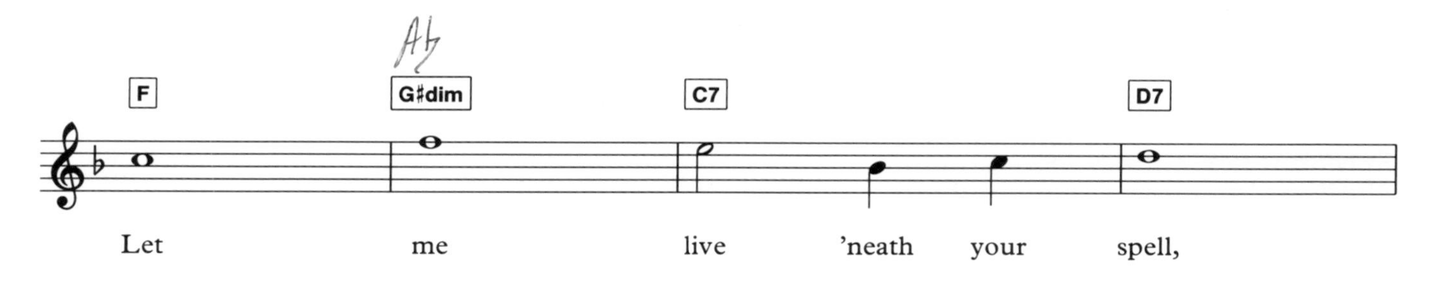
F
G♯dim
C7
D7
Let me live 'neath your spell,

C♯
C
B♭
do do___ that voo - doo___ that you do___ so

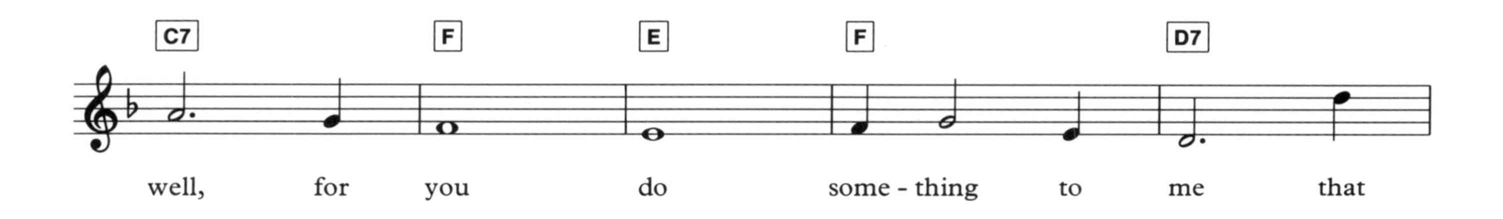
C7
F
E
F
D7
well, for you do some - thing to me that

G7
C7
F
B♭
F
no - bo - dy else could do.___

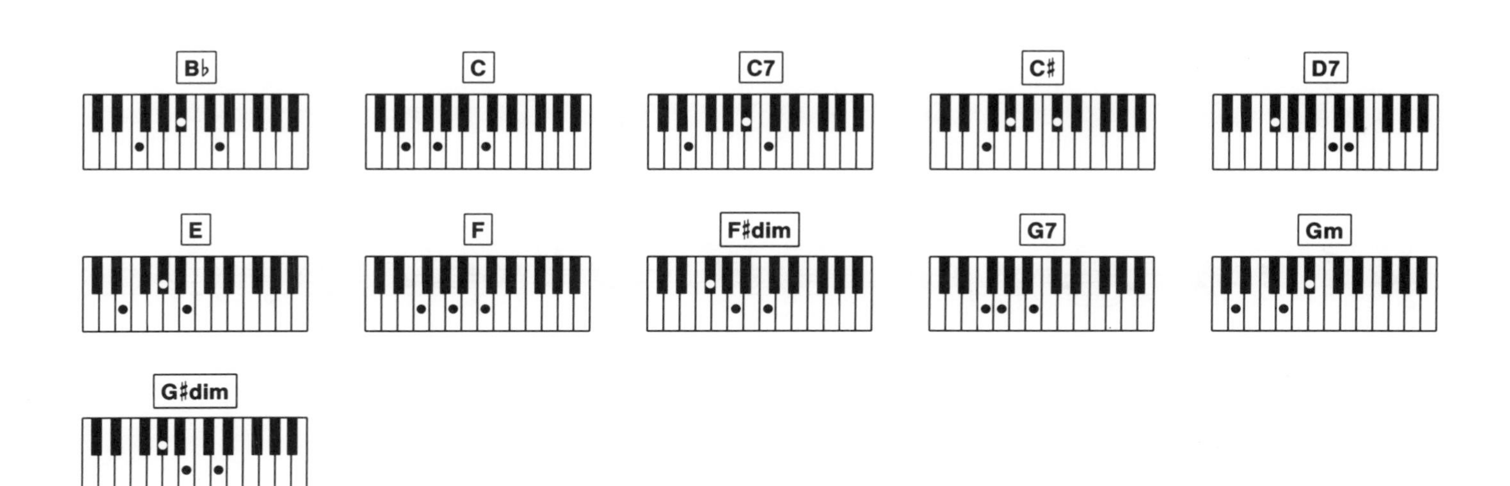
B♭
C
C7
C♯
D7
E
F
F♯dim
G7
Gm
G♯dim

YOU'LL NEVER KNOW

Words by Mack Gordon
Music by Harry Warren

Suggested Registration: Clarinet
Rhythm: Swing
Tempo: ♩ = 98

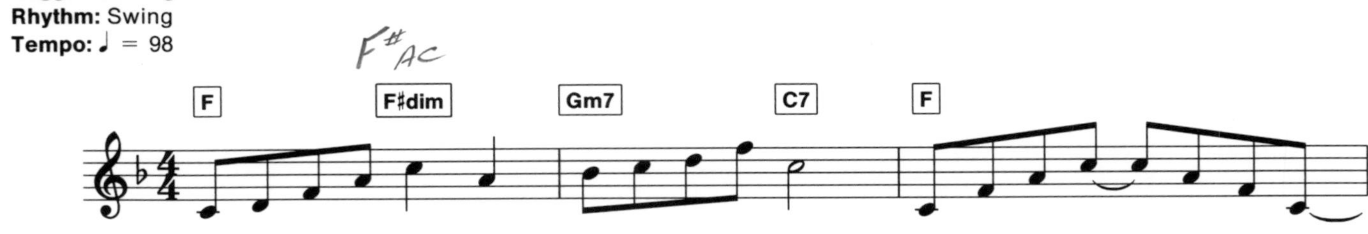

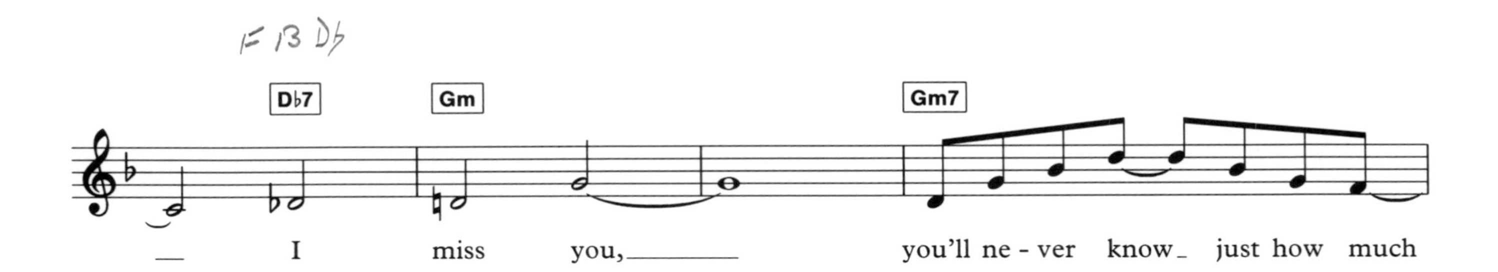

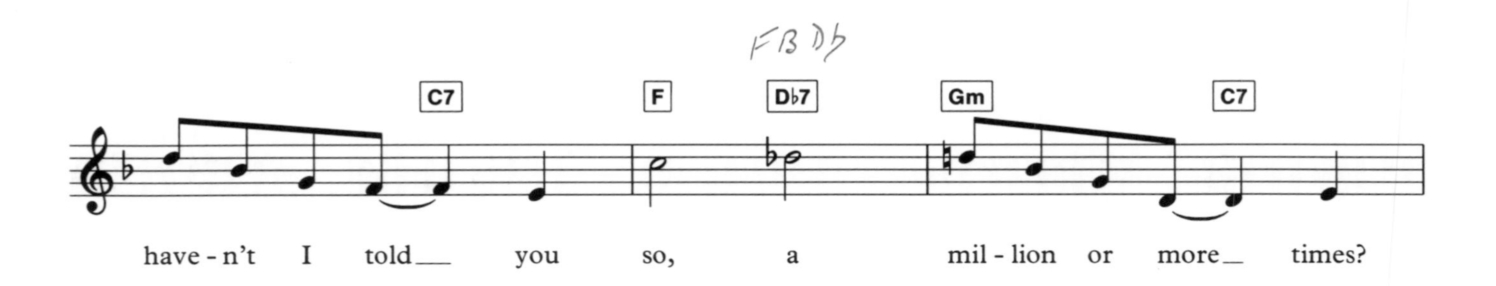

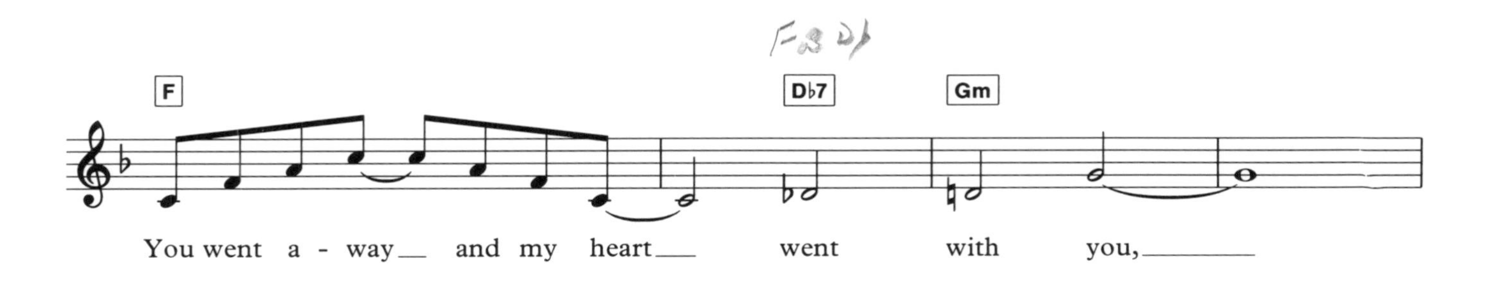
F
D♭7
Gm
You went a - way and my heart went with you,

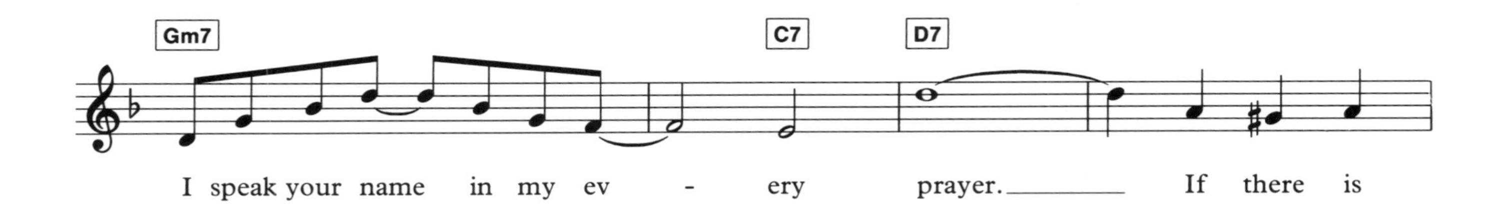
Gm7
C7
D7
I speak your name in my ev - ery prayer. If there is

Gm7
B♭m
F
A7
D7
some oth-er way to prove that I love you, I swear I don't know how,

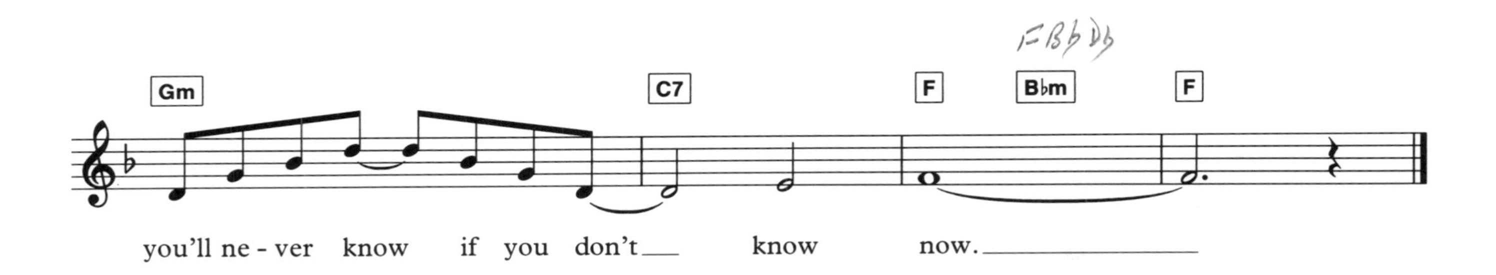
Gm
C7
F
B♭m
F
you'll ne - ver know if you don't know now.

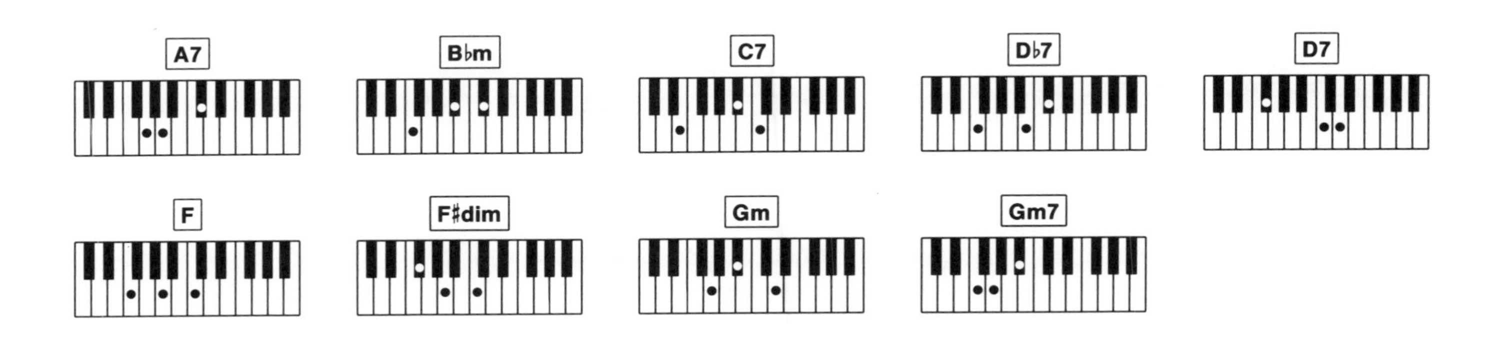
A7
B♭m
C7
D♭7
D7
F
F♯dim
Gm
Gm7

Younger Than Springtime

Words by Oscar Hammerstein II
Music by Richard Rodgers

Suggested Registration: Vibraphone
Rhythm: Swing
Tempo: ♩ = 104

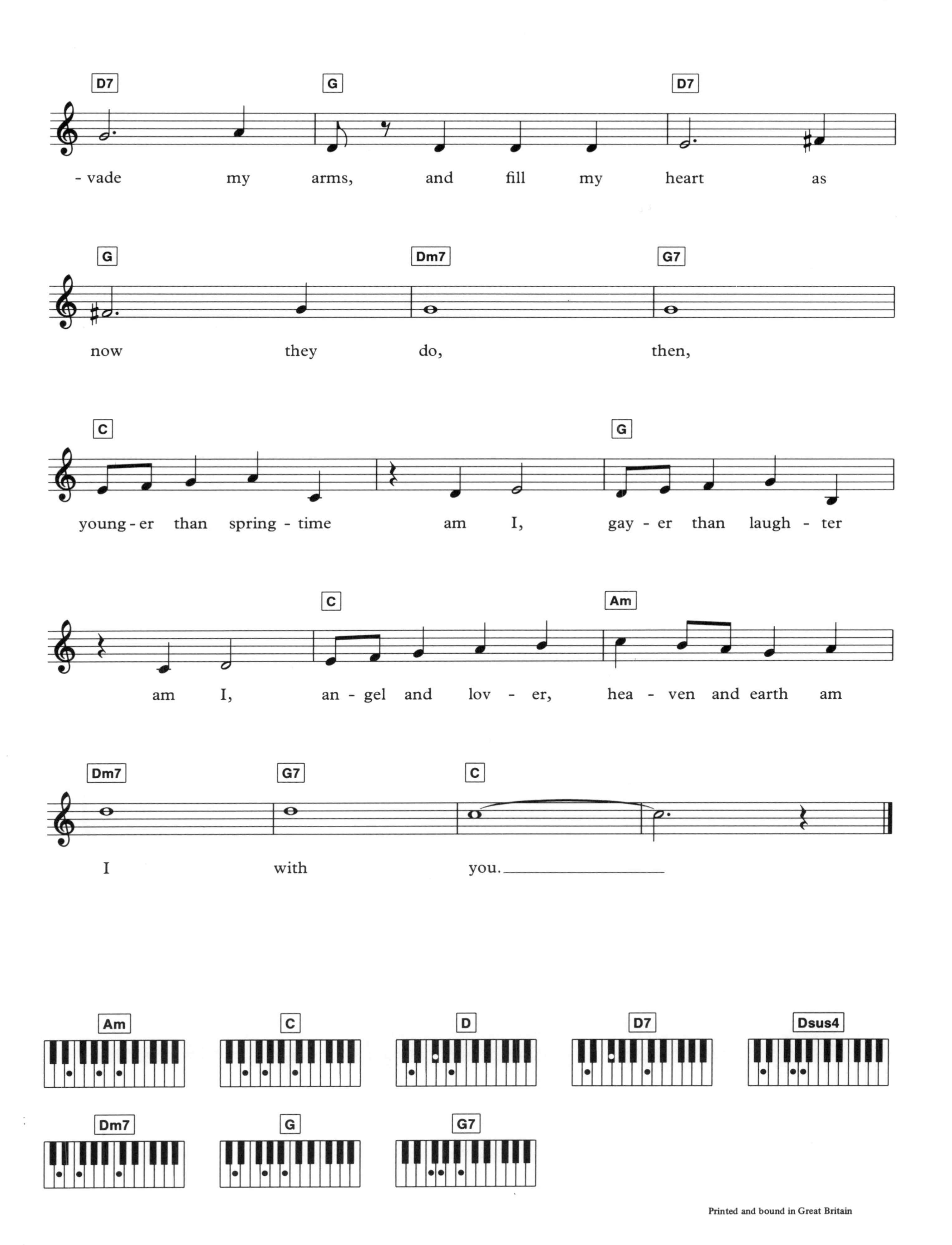

Printed and bound in Great Britain

The Easy Keyboard Library 

An expansive series of over 50 titles!

Each song features melody line, vocals, chord displays, suggested registrations and rhythm settings.

"For each title ALL the chords (both 3 finger and 4 finger) used
are shown in the correct position – which makes a change!"
Organ & Keyboard Cavalcade

Each song appears on two facing pages,
eliminating the need to turn the page during performance.

The 00s
Big Band Hits
Billy Joel
Blues
Broadway
Celebration Songs
Christmas Carols
Christmas Songs
Classic Hits Vol 1
Classic Hits Vol 2
Cliff Richard
Cole Porter
Country Songs
Disco
The Eighties
The Essential Chord Dictionary
Favourite Hymns
The Fifties
Film Classics
The Forties
Frank Sinatra
George & Ira Gershwin
George Michael
Gilbert & Sullivan
Glenn Miller
Great Songwriters
I Try & 10 More Chart Hits
Instrumental Classics
James Bond
Jazz Classics
Latin Collection
Love Songs Vol 1
Love Songs Vol 2
Motown Classics
Music Hall
Nat King Cole
The Nineties
No.1 Hits Vol 1
No.1 Hits Vol 2
Popular Classics
Pub Singalong Collection
Queen
Rock 'n' Roll Classics
Scott Joplin
The Seventies
Shirley Bassey
Showtunes Vol 1
The Sixties
Soft Rock Collection
Soul Classics
The Thirties
Traditional Irish Favourites
TV Themes
The Twenties
Wartime Collection
West End Hits
Whitney Houston

To buy Faber Music publications or to find out about the full range of titles available
please contact your local music retailer or Faber Music sales enquiries:

Faber Music Ltd, Burnt Mill, Elizabeth Way, Harlow CM20 2HX
Tel: +44 (0) 1279 82 89 82 Fax: +44 (0) 1279 82 89 83
sales@fabermusic.com fabermusic.com expressprintmusic.com